THE JOURNAL OF
MARY HERVEY RUSSELL

BOOKS BY STORM JAMESON

Novels of Personal Life
 That was Yesterday
 A Day off
 Delicate Monster
 Farewell, Night ; Welcome, Day

Novels of the Crisis
 Company Parade
 Love in Winter
 None Turn Back
 In the Second Year
 Europe to Let
 Cousin Honoré
 The Fort
 Then We Shall Hear Singing
 Cloudless May

Miscellaneous
 Modern Drama in Europe
 No Time Like the Present
 Civil Journey
 The End of This War (P.E.N. book)

THE JOURNAL
OF
MARY HERVEY
RUSSELL

BY

STORM JAMESON

LONDON
MACMILLAN · & CO. LTD
1945

COPYRIGHT

PRINTED IN GREAT BRITAIN
BY R. & R. CLARK, LIMITED, EDINBURGH

For Do

" Returning to darkness, the consoling mother,
For the short winter sleep. . . ."

" La vie d'un homme est son image. A l'heure de mourir, nous nous refléterons dans le passé, et, penchés sur le miroir de nos actes, nos âmes reconnaîtront *ce que nous sommes*. Toute notre vie s'emploie à tracer de nous-mêmes un ineffaçable portrait. Le terrible, c'est qu'on ne le sait pas ; on ne songe pas à se faire beau. On y songe en parlant de soi ; on se flatte ; mais notre terrible portrait, plus tard, ne nous flattera pas. On raconte sa vie et l'on se ment ; mais notre vie ne mentira pas ; elle racontera notre âme, qui se présentera devant Dieu dans sa posture habituelle."

GIDE, *Journal 1889–1939*

FIRST BOOK

Bordeaux, June 14.

Four o'clock in the afternoon, on the Quai de Richelieu, waiting to cross the Pont de Pierre — the heat is scarcely endurable, a transparent mask pressed on eyes and head ; the traffic strangles itself in noise, heat, fumes of oil and petrol. Suddenly, with all this, slipping through some tear in the web, a strong scent of lime blossom. Yes, there is a tree in full bloom. This country cannot help pressing a joy into your hand even at an unlikely moment.

*

I look everywhere, feeling certain that my mother must have sat in this garden in the Place Gambetta. It is exactly the place she looked for in a foreign town, and enjoyed with every sense. Folding her sunshade, she would sit on one of these iron chairs made to imitate cane — chestnut-trees grow thickly at this side, offering the shade needed by her fine northern skin — and look at this magnolia-tree in bloom, at the grass, freshly green round the flower-beds, and the minuscule stream and lake. At the same time, crown and deep reason of her joy, she had within sight and hearing the restless life of Bordeaux, noisy trams, the café at the corner of the Cours de Tourny, shops with their motionless sun-blinds.

Silent, eagerness itself behind her reserve, she looked in every port for some new thing. That double window of hats and blouses : she certainly stared into it a dozen times before going inside to point, with a mute desperate arrogance, at handkerchiefs. Perhaps in the end she bought other things : in those days she was still a dandy, loving delicate fashionable clothes — and forced to contrive in order to have them. Yes, yes, she must have come here. Then why am I not sure which was her chosen place ? She chose one and returned to it day after day, as long as her husband's ship stayed in port — this side of a public garden rather than that, this café and this table in it, this street of shops. Why cannot I be sure of her in the Place Gambetta ?

I

Since she was here, I suppose about 1890, the names of some of the streets have been changed. Not that that will disconcert her. She rarely troubled to learn the name of a street, expecting the cab-men to know by instinct that she wished to be set down in the best shopping street. Or if she were going back to the ship, that they would understand the words spoken in her strongest voice — " Go to the Prince Line dock." I suppose they knew the habits of English captains' wives.

*

In the late dusk when I went back to my hotel I looked at things for her, in the hope that, seeing them through my eyes, she would recollect herself and come forward. Turning out of the Cours du Jardin Publique — now Cours de Verdun, but she would prefer the more modest name — into a narrow street, I saw with startled joy the Monument des Girondins profiled white against the sky. Later, from the window of my bedroom on a corner of the Place des Quinconces, I watched the lights blazing outside the theatre — they should be gas-lamps — and along the quays, those on the farther side of the Garonne reflected in the past, in her present. A dialogue between a piano and a violin began in the large café at a corner — endlessly continued, using up what little air, what little darkness, there was.

I was sleepless — not only because of the breathless heat, but I feared to overlook the one thing that was keeping her and meaning to give her up in its own time. And Bordeaux scarcely slept. The café was awake until long after midnight, and at three o'clock men were sweeping the streets, and talking, between it and the river. Very early, almost before dawn, the lamps still burning along the quays, but as if abolished already by the still absent light, a single star, immense, appeared over the harbour. I watched a little colour come into the sky — as stealthy as that which unbelievably came back after she died, only to her cheeks, not her far too suave mouth — above the shadow formed of trees and houses crowding the other bank of the river. In a few minutes there was a full chorus of birds in the Place des Quinconces, the star dwindled to a dot, the street-lamps went out on the quays, flicked off by a thumb. Stretch-

ing itself, the light pushed the sky away on all sides, and just
after four the sun sprang from the Garonne directly into my
room. I ought now to have closed the shutters, but I was too
eager. Abroad, I am very much the captain's wife in my
curiosity : which is at its most alert in towns : it seizes its chance
to sleep when I take it to the country.

Bordeaux was making signs and I could not read them.
The conversation went on outside, growing more lively and
complicated — a plume of factory smoke in the clear sky ;
cranes leaning over the unruffled brightness of the river ; oddly
cut down by the sun, the two lighthouse-columns ; the breeze,
only audible where it crossed the branches of a tree ; the traffic
thickening with every minute ; a girl and a young man laughing together on their way to work ; men in washed-out blouses :
above them all, an incessant darting and crossing of noisy
shuttles, the swifts.

By seven o'clock the heat was frightful, the Garonne had
lost its colour — a breath of mist clouded the glass. I closed
both shutters, but the heat had settled itself firmly in the room ;
it clung to the heavy gilt overmantel and the stains on rose-
flowered carpet and wall-paper. I felt ill, and rang for coffee
to pull me together.

When the chambermaid came in, she looked at me and said,
" Il fait chaud à Bordeaux." At once, as though the words,
opening a door in one of the deeper caves of my mind, had
released a memory living now with all the energy of an intuition,
one I could not refuse, since it helped itself to every sense as
well as every fibre of intellect, I was sure that my mother had
stayed here. Sometimes, if the ship were lying a long way
down the river from a town she liked, she would leave it and
stay in an hotel. This was exactly the type of modest middle-
class hotel she would choose. Had she, too, been unable to
sleep for the heat and told me about it in one of the rare moments
when she spoke of her voyages ? Repeating words she had
understood, but was not willing to reply to except by one of
her brief smiles and an involuntarily haughty glance — all too
English, the chambermaid must have thought.

Very well, if she stayed here, she went out after breakfast —

defying the heat — and straight to the Allées de Tourny. Not only is it just round the corner but it is the widest and most opulent of Bordeaux's streets.

I went there, and looked in every shop for just that object, a flower or a hat, which in any foreign street sums up its foreignness. There was a moment when I thought I had her. She stepped forward, reflected in the glass of the window. . . . No one. Myself. . . . I am an idiot — when she meant seriously to buy anything, she looked for it in this side-street of more modest shops. In front of the dark narrow glove-shop I felt for the first time certain that the young woman I never knew had come here : it was a very old shop. I went in and began looking at gloves ; I chose a pair in white doe-skin for my youngest sister : she, they say, who is most like my mother as a girl.

She stood here, I thought, and turned over pair after pair of gloves, not willing to explain in English what she wanted and because of the silence she must oppose to her volubility very cold towards the woman ; at last she chose a pair, glancing, mistrustful, at the price, then doubled her hand for the glove to be measured across her knuckles. Still guarded, she smiled for the first time when the woman blew chalk into the fingers and stretched them on wooden tongs. She refused to have them fitted, and carried them to the garden of the Place Gambetta ; there, with infinite pains, each finger smoothed down and the thumb left out until the last, she tried them. A success ? The money not wasted ? . . . Content, lightly happy behind her remote gaze, she relaxed and gave Bordeaux its head.

*

Les Eyzies, July.

I shall not believe that men lived, yes, lived at the ends of these long galleries in the rock — a primitive civilisation of a much higher order produced the drawings of animals on the walls. Nor do I believe that the artists were moved by anything less strong than the pleasure of creating an object they could look at, detached from themselves. The actual drawings and paintings, by the way, and the copies made of them, are no alike. The originals are rougher and incomplete, with a childish severity the copies smooth out.

The same impulse to explain, and explain away, is responsible for the idea, puerile, that *homo Mousteriensis* made his drawings because he believed they would help him in some magical way with his hunting. The hunter lived his knowledge of the animal, or dreamed it. One day a man found pleasure in *knowing* his knowledge, in separating it from himself, so that he knew it in a new way and loved it with a new love. The step from the primitive to the speculative use of the mind had been taken. It was a step away from the magical use of the sign (to act upon nature) and towards the disinterested use — as knowledge, the act by which the artist enters into the object, and the work of art is conceived in and born from it. If his fellow primitives, or many of them, or sometimes, mistook his disinterested signs for magical ones, it would not be surprising. It is surprising that we fall into the same error. I am sure that what he deeply wanted to do was to detach as many things from himself as possible. The first, it is also the pure impulse of art. Before an object can be taken into the mind, and before it can be created, it must be, if only for a moment, detached. The great artists are those who have separated from themselves a universe of objects, so that they have created or re-discovered an inner world, where they move freely — noticing how from a certain angle or in certain moments this object resembles one other or a great many, how they vibrate into each other and affect the eye so that for the future it sees differently : the folds of a woman's dress as ribbed sand ; or the sea, the stones of a graveyard, the conscious mind, as surfaces which, if questioned, will give up the same metaphysical image ; or pity is seen to be another face of contempt. His hardest effort gives, as object, to the artist, himself : he is at last free.

This attempt, always renewed in the generations of writers and readers, was certainly being made in the caves of the Vézère valley, by a prehistoric Frenchman — already, by that clear and massive sunlight, told to think without more ambiguity than one needs to explain what finally is inexplicable : why the human mind should delight in representing to itself what it sees, and what it feels, why it cannot be content to live absorbed in the universe, why it must begin its work of detaching things from itself and having begun, seek, often to exhaustion, to make a whole out of what it knows to be only fragments. Why ?

Looking at the cave drawings of la Mouthe, I realised the vanity of my hard work. I shall never advance very far in detachment. A decade and a half of almost incessant work have only brought me to the point where I see what a writer is — and see in the same moment that I was never a writer nor shall be. Once I had too much to learn, but then a certain moment was reached when I had too much to unlearn. And now there would be no time — lacking exceptional powers of concentration. May I be born again, remembering my mistake ! (O but to live it all over again — even with so much that was joyful and simple — would one have the strength ?)

*

He took an extreme pride, this uneducated director of a steel works, in the very complicated and beautiful machines and machine-tools, designed or perfected in his works. At first I thought they are in some sense or on some level the counterpart today of Renaissance sculpture. The marvellous organisation of the human body, as it was grasped and, in his way served, by Michelangelo, is a machine comparable in grandeur with these. But more love, and a finer, because disinterested courage, went into the construction of his symbols of David and Moses and the others. We are forced, in describing the work of design and labour, to use the same word for sculpture and machine-tool. They are both of them constructions.

Then I noticed how puerile, placed beside the machines of this factory, are such works as the kinetic sculpture of Moholy-Nagy, and the different yet essentially similar work of the Constructivists — yes, they even call themselves or are called by this name which challenges them to an effort of organisation as great as that of the unnamed designer of these machines and tools. How childish, in comparison, is their response. . . . But what I want is to understand the nature, the final impulse, of abstract sculpture and painting. It is not something to condemn, but

6

to be wrestled with. It has a human value. . . . We forget that some of our values belong to death.

Is not abstract art the statement purely of relations ? Are not the forms of a Hepworth, a Rodchenko, an Arp, the schemes of a mind which creates by reducing to a few the multiple powers of the object ? The mind's creative effort is directed as purely as possible to its relation with the ideal skeleton, the Idea. The next and logical move would be towards an empty space in which, undistorted by the need to express itself through any matter, the pure form, realised in the mind of the artist or in the mind of an ideal spectator in harmony with his, would exist solely by its absence. (Am I mistaken in my memory of an emptily white canvas ? By Mondrian ? By some artist whose name I have forgotten ?) The analogy with the poetry of Mallarmé is too clear to be missed. Would not an abstract painter or sculptor find his keenest pleasure in thinking,

> *plus longtemps peut-être éperdûment*
> *A l'autre, au sein brûlé d'une antique Amazone ?*

And would he not feel that the forms realised by a Pavlova, and ceasing in the very instant of creation, are closer to his ideal than any he can fix in stone or wood ?

By a usual paradox, the purity of the mind's effort is subordinated to nature in the abstract sculptor's obedience to the nature of his materials. The less pure artist disregards in them any quality he does not need in order to construct ; they obey him, they become at once less and more than themselves : he is able to give to the *organisation* of sensations and thoughts the energy the abstract sculptor spends in submitting to the nature of wood, stone, granite.

In attempting to realise a pure method, the artist approaches the philosopher, whose effort is to know, rather than to construct. Abstract art is a statement of what is. It is representational by the method of algebra. It excludes memory and expectation, the past and the future, all that estate and playground of the artist which consists in what is not already here, given. (Or rather, does not his most serious play consist in leading what *is* into these other states, a ceaseless movement back and forth, between being and absence ?) It states a few of the relationships of volume, surface, position, light. But to construct is to do more than make a statement, and more than to note in colour or line an algebraic formula, and more than to realise by setting it up a problem in geometry. Out of the block of relations thus stated, the artist who constructs (not the Constructivist !) evokes a new and fecund object : between it and the spectators an image or an order of images is born, and which move *comme les meut l'objet aimé.*

The speculations of the abstract artist's mind — sterile until entering and being entered into by the senses, the body, to create between them a precise play of forces and a deliberate illusion — produce a formula which is too pure to act. (In the preface Valéry wrote to a book by, I think, Lucien Fabre, I came on this sentence : *Rien de si pur ne peut coexister avec les conditions de la vie. Nous traversons seulement l'idée de la perfection, comme la main impunément tranche la flamme.*) And strangely, the purity of his work is not what he believes it to be. Abstract art is the slave of matter. It arrests movement in the object of its contemplation, justly affirming its identity — $x = x$ — but denying its inter-relations with the rest of the universe (inner and outer). By a natural paradox, the effort to make a purely intellectual gesture has fallen into its equally sterile opposite : a purely material one results. The artist who is satisfied to make a statement is giving himself a satisfaction. Pure art ? Or is he the type of Onan ? Let me look again at one of these Constructivist objects, a Form, a single shaft of wood, polished, by Barbara Hepworth. To admire it, I must set in motion my own rational pleasure in a statement of relations. I must make the mental effort to re-state them. There is no relation between my mind and the artist's, though I persuade myself that one takes place. I, too, have carried out a sterile act.

Sterility. The unconscious revolt against it led to surrealism — the attempt to lead back into the object those of its powers which had been abstracted. And, since it was the motion in reverse of an intellectual act, it was sensational and archaic. Surrealism, in painting or literature, sprang from a profound troubling of the human spirit. Its first confused gestures were seized on and imitated by the impulse which drives women and advertising agents to run after a fashion and police it to their use. It became stereotyped at a very shallow level of discovery. The descent into the self usually reaches no farther than the most trivial memories of representational art, fragments broken off Victorian monuments, photographic reproduction of objects, landscapes less truthful than coloured postcards. Impatience, the commercial desire for quick results, has closed or is closing with this rubble steps by which a new divinity — *une profonde enfant* — might reach the light.

The paradox of surrealism, in art or poetry, is that its quality depends not singly on the power with which the subconscious image, the dream, is charged, but on the strength and subtlety of the conscious intelligence which receives and works on it. Moreover, the irrational sign is not made by a primitive imagination, rich in concrete experiences of a world in which sense and symbol are vitally fused. The evolved intellect, speculative and practical, has taken up into itself a vast psychic energy which cannot be turned back into the irrational, but can be used to explore, subtilise, and conceive enduring forms for the energies which spring from a source deeper than itself, and deeper than the dream.

Everywhere in these years, not only in the books we live with and the paintings we admire, we are faced by the refusal of the intellect to understand the flesh. This refusal, made, if it is honest, without contempt, is the nature itself of the intellect. Does not the artist exist only to overcome the consequences of this natural inclination of his reason ? To pose to himself the problems raised by the real existence of an infinite number of subtly organised bodies, and to solve them by the method of his art ? And the nature of this method ? Neither abstraction of sensual motion, nor a smuggling of part of it back in popular surrealism. A deep attention, the liveliest and most wilful curiosity, and the most profitable, almost an act of love, giving immediate knowledge of the creature loved.

This absence of love terribly equals a presence of fear. Fear is the deep motive of abstract art — fear of a repellent civilisation which is dominated by the power of things. Driven by his unacknowledged fear, the artist's intellect begins the effort of abstraction which finally imprisons him in the object, in his statements. His fearful struggle, to avoid being implicated, implicates him always more hopelessly in objects he cannot dominate, but must obey. He suffers now

> *Pour n'avoir pas chanté la région où vivre*
> *Quand du stérile hiver a resplendi l'ennui.*

And who can be surprised if, more sensitive than the others, the artist is terrified by the power things have acquired over us ? A day will surely come, years from now, when those pausing in front of them in museums will say, of these faceless Profiles and skeletal Forms, " How the artists of that time starved themselves, and filtered everything before tasting it ! How much fear they swallowed with every particle of life, and how, turning their backs on the present, they found that both the future they dreaded, and the past, were deserting them, and there was nowhere they could live safely, except in just that metaphysical point to which they clung and gave birth to their sterile thoughts. All their strength went into denying what they feared, and hated because of it. They had none left over for the effort of construction."

Which will arrive first, artists who are brave enough to rejoice, or a world to rejoice in ?

*

The other day I was forced to come into the open and quarrel with an older, infinitely more powerful person — a man who as well as being bad-tempered and arbitrary, is an individual, very rare these days.

I knew as soon as I took my place at the head of the long table — it was a committee, and these are an ordeal to my growing fear of people — that there was going to be trouble, and I repeated to myself : You are the last voice on earth of your mother Sylvia Russell and Mary Hervey her mother. This gave me courage : I could not very well disgrace these two shades, both so headstrong and outspoken and, especially the last, formidable.

The trouble began at once, when he accused me of sub-
servience to the Foreign Office, of plotting to bring our innocent
society under ministerial control. The accusation was grotesque,
the fantasy of a strong lively mind twisted by its suspicions.
There were foreigners at the table. They were distressed, and
their deep respect for him kept them mute ; facing their silence,
I had either to oppose or give way to him.

My need to be approved of is terrible. Alone in my room,
writing, I can be honest. I say " honest " — but sometimes the
effect is not what I meant, and I am accused, to my extreme
astonishment, of violence. Violence ? My whole instinct is
towards pleasing people ; I dread, worse than anything, their
disapproval. There, there, good dog, I say to the beast I see
coming into the room with another person. I smile, nod, make
propitiating signs with my voice. I behave as I do with all except
the few close friends in whose hands — with due regard for
politeness — I can risk the truth. . . . My heinous wish to be
liked, my fear of disapproval and anger, form a part, inseparable,
of my anxious wish for these almost strangers to feel happy.
An image of myself comes forward to serve them with anything
they need to feel pleased with themselves. My self disappears.
I have no idea what it does, or how it excuses itself for its
cowardice and indiscipline. I do not always succeed ; at these
times something must have betrayed me. That disobedient
violence ?

Today — thanks to the support of my two shades — I was
able to seem calm and scarcely to feel my ordinary terror at the
sound of a raised voice. He became milder and repeated, " I
don't like the way you're going." I had an impulse to tell
him that I admired his willingness to be quarrelled with. Instead
— " You talk," I heard myself say, " like my mother." An
extraordinary thing to say ; where on earth did it come from ?
The ridiculous dispute went on, past the cautious faces of the
foreigners, with bent heads evading the anglo-saxon lightnings.
Can I be learning courage ? Or is it simply that when there is
no hope for it, no hope of pleasing, when I am savaged by an
opponent plainly not to be soothed, I make the best of a bad job ?

In the end, he said he was leaving us, we had abandoned him.

I protested that it was we who were being abandoned. "No, no," he said, "it is a parting," and rose to go. I stood up — and stood while he gathered his overcoat and gas-mask. He lectured us, smiling, on our duty to carry gas-masks. I opened the door, we shook hands ; he went. None of the others, English or foreigners, seemed sorry ; they stretched themselves and smiled. I was so sad that it cost me an effort not to show it. To think that of all writers in the world I had chosen this one for my unlikely courage — the one who influenced my adolescence, changed it and my life. (For that I owe him no thanks, but is he responsible for what I made of myself ?) A few months before this, I had asked him to approve of a difficult and drastic action I wanted to take in this society. He said : Certainly, he would do anything he could, "though I am an old worn-out man, and may drop dead at any moment. What would you do if I dropped dead now ? "

"I should cry for my lost youth," I said, almost without thought.

"Ah." He did not seem vexed — but I could not read his expression, I know of him only what is obvious. . . . It is true that he was in some way our youth, the youth of those whom two wars have eaten. Could he not have been content — clearly, disgust with the world is the root of his arbitrary ways and many suspicions — could he not, I thought sadly, be content with having changed the mental habits of more young men and young women than any writer since Rousseau ? No, of course not — he wanted them to do him credit. Alas, so many of them were killed before they had time to show whether they were fit for that. He is defeated now by the tolerance of our English governments, who despise writers too much even to suppress them. Unlike that other fountain of ideas, Bernard Shaw, he cannot console himself by clowning. His seriousness was one of the qualities we liked in him : the young do not care for mountebanks. And now this fantastic dispute !

I console myself that probably he has not left — except for a short time, to punish us.

*

Usually when she had to see or when she thought about her

first husband she felt a sense of guilt, as though in some way she were to blame for everything — it was astonishing how large a part guilt played in her deep life : very often she felt most guilty towards acts which, if she were to talk about them, would surely have been justified by her listeners, as they had been by events. But it would be she who was telling the story, and it was she who had caused to happen the events which seemed to justify her. Only she knew how treacherously she had behaved. But what if it were all she knew about herself? There is as much vanity in self-scourgings as in self-justification. She was good at both.

On this occasion she felt neither guilt nor weakness. He was so confident, boisterous even ; she felt as never before how few impulses they had in common. (What they had once in common was first youth, its egoism, fevers, and unmanageable energy. But that is the most usual of accidents.) He insisted with great good-humour on making the forty minutes' journey back with her. When she had got home she was worn out, and aware of a dreadful disturbance taking place in some part of her mind. No one noticed it. How could they? — it was buried as deeply as any moment of childhood.

Like all such moments, it chose the darkness, when she was lying in bed, to come to the surface. It was still faceless, a vast stifling cocoon of unmotived sadness — no, no, a cocoon is not alive, and this was living and active in the lowest depths of her life at the same time when it was holding open her eyelids and squeezing her throat. She tried repeating : *In returning and rest ye shall be saved, in quietness and in confidence shall be your strength.* It was useless? Return where? To childhood? To her first years of marriage? The thought that if she cried she would only be crying for herself kept her from just that folly. She felt her heart being torn out, examined, and thrust back anyhow, by a brutal hand. Let me sleep, she begged, only let me sleep. And at last she was set down, and slept.

It often seemed to her that she had spent her life creating what she could not, when it chose to make itself felt, control. Terrifying to think of this growing in her, one day, perhaps, o break out and devour all it saw. But that was unlikely —

she was not one of those headstrong people who become desperate. She had too much alloy in her metal.

*

Four Germans, refugees, spent the evening with us. I knew one of them well, the least dependent, the only one who is free and ruthless ; it was she who brought the others. Of them, one, a Jewish musician, had gaiety and courage, another was still so afraid that when I dropped a spoon he turned pale and shuddered violently : the third, his wife, was very young, vague, with dark eyes that were a little mad, and charmingly rosy cheeks. She was timidly silent. I devoted myself to her, leaving the others to a discussion which became more and more passionate — they were happy at least — and in the end she was talking simply and gaily. After a time her countrywoman noticed it and drew me aside. " Why do you bother with her ? " she said fiercely : " it is quite unnecessary, she is not used to being taken notice of." The other young woman had not heard. Fortunately.

I set myself the task of giving each of them in turn his proper importance. It is so simple that you can scarcely make a mistake. You have only to listen and become nothing or a mirror, in which they see themselves before they were refugees. When they had gone I felt myself as hollow as a reed, and at the same time exhausted, and scattered about a continent. As very slowly I washed cups and glasses, swept up tobacco ash, and straightened chairs, the scattered pieces returned to their places. But it had been, I might even say, a near thing.

*

When I feel responsible for other people's happiness, when I use every effort to help them, making myself nothing, giving away will and time, it is not kindness, it is part of my fear. Where can I have laid in such a stock of fear ? And how is it that it remains at the same level, though it is used from every day ?

*

When I think of my ancestors, the men and women whose portraits I have seen — and about many of them stories were told to us which made them figures of legend and no less alive for that — I know that if I were to meet them I should dislike extremely their smiling, almost brutal irony, their contempt for what could not be handled in the form of heavy silver spoons and tea-pots, or launched in the small shipyard, or banked. The air of shrewd malice in the back of their eyes kills anything which is not as robust as they are and as direct. These eccentric men, whose rages and headstrong actions were really the amusements they had thought of to save themselves from boredom — they were terribly easily bored — these domineering women, whose daughters somehow were not crushed but grew up to rule families in their turn : how I should have hated them and with respect and envy. They were certainly masters, even of their own violent natures ; they allowed these to behave with a savage oddity only because it relieved them of themselves for a few hours. And because there was more space in the world in those days, and on the whole they were admired as eccentrics — by everyone, perhaps, except by the sons and daughters they would have destroyed if most of these young ones had not been as hard as themselves and inured to whippings and sarcasm.

But why did I write : If I were to meet them ? I meet them every time jeering laughter springs in me when I am asked to share emotions involving an image of myself as sensitive, high-minded, suffering from my passions and the tragedy of our times. The moment this image is noticed by all those pairs of malicious eyes, I am seized by a laughter which is nothing better than a devil, a ridiculous jeering mean *northern* devil. This morning I had a letter from a man I knew when we were both young and have not seen for years. He wrote it because he knew that with the outbreak of another war I should be feeling despair. Despair, anguish, fear — yes, all those feelings. They are under my pillow. . . . I had a moment of genuine kindness ; it was, I think, chiefly for myself, the young woman who has learned as clumsy and stupid people do, by running 'nto things. But then I caught sight of the image, and an uncontrolled laughter broke out of me, almost broke me. It did not stop until everything was destroyed.

*

There are times when the whole world is only the appearance taken by my sorrow for her death. The sunlight, the green trees, are a horrible vacancy.

I sit here writing. Outside, the garden has a cool glittering freshness, there is a smell of lilac — if I get up I shall see the tree, as if dazed by the sunlight and its weight of flowers. And I see, I feel, that we are seated in the early train going to Scarborough. The train is standing in a little station, the last before we reach Scarborough ; the sun shines like this sun on its trees and flower-beds. My mother is sitting opposite me : for a second, and without effort except this pang, I can create her out of the surface of a particular dress, a gesture, hand shut on the clasp of a bag, air of absorbed expectation. So far we have been lucky — until this moment a carriage to ourselves for the hour's journey along the coast ; between gorse, windy fields, the sea, always the sea, suave promise of sun for the whole of this day out.

The train will go on, into Scarborough. We shall get out and hurry down Westborough to Rowntree's. First, the ritual cup of coffee, then the slow, relentlessly slow, progress through all the floors of the large shop. Especially we examine the dozens of chairs, tables, settees. She has always, folded in her like the kernel of a grain, the idea of a house where every object is perfect. And while during visit after visit she seeks, some fragment of the ideal takes shape before her — then she must consider, go away, come back and look again, and again, and at last, when she, I, and the assistant who has known her for so many years, are all on the point of exhaustion, she decides. It is the same with the hat she will buy downstairs, or at Marshall's. In both shops, the patient heads of departments take trouble with her. We sit surrounded by hats. She leans to look deeply into the mirror, and not as though she were seeing herself. In search rather of the *other* ; and fixedly, of the life she in some moment, on her way here, had overlooked — and perhaps expecting to catch a last glimpse of it. . . . I am desperately anxious for her to enjoy one of those triumphs on which she will congratulate herself, with her distant smile, on the journey home. I get up and look about myself for the perfect hat, I exclaim, and support her when she hesitates over the price of a " model ". I know she will regret endlessly not choosing it. Once, when the hat she coveted, on which many strands of ospreys had been stitched singly, was dear beyond anything, I whispered to her confidently that I could copy it. I am so awkward at sewing that I could never learn, but the agonising need to please her inspired me : it was a success, marvellous, and for a whole summer she wore it with her joy in a new elegance.

And then, the other streets and shops, and lunch. If her favourite table is still vacant, I rush to snatch it from the couple making in a leisurely way towards it. In the afternoon the antique shops, where also we are known, and the rest, before the train, in the rose-garden. O streets I shall never walk in without you, with you and not able to see you, not hear, not ever carry that burden again, nor ever lay it down. Never again, never, never.

Nothing in the way of success coming to me has any taste when I cannot show it to you. You never knew how little certain successes meant, how far I am from achievement. To you they were really triumphs, and you took them into your hands with the same sharp happiness, the same comforting sense of security, that filled you when at last I was just able to give you the fur coat promised for " when my ship comes in ". Now if it comes in, you are not on the quay, not in the house waiting, you are nowhere.

If, during the last year, even the last week, I had not felt that you were an importunate child, and O grief, neglected you. . . .

*

In February of the year before Hitler seized power, when I went to Berlin, I walked into a surrealist landscape. Here were the same scattered objects, at first glance meaningless, coldly separate, or joined in equivocal ways ; and the deliberate outrage of custom in manners and arts, with submission, help-less, to conventions — of speed, perversion, and a primitive religion. Unrelated activities ran temperatures and nursed them in rooms of a reassuring vulgarity — less reassuring when one of them split in half to display a suicide or an adultery : as little as possible was concealed : frankness, the evacuation of all ideas and instincts, was part of the nightmare.

There was the Sport-palast, where relays of young men had cycled day and night without a break, for six days. During the hours the place was crammed with spectators the teams raced each other ; they put on spurts announced by the loud-speaker ; when one of them finished his turn he stopped his machine at a cubicle between the track and the tiers of seats, and fell on to his bunk, his joints gone, the yellow unresistant flesh of his legs and stomach dull even when slapped and kneaded with oil. I watched a young man leave his cubicle when his name was shouted by the crowd : his girl tried to pat his arm, he brushed her away peevishly, he had become a machine whose legs unrolled a strip of track, under the fierce lights, between cliffs honeycombed with mouths yelling and swallowing down beer and sausages : after breakfast — some of the spectators stayed through the night and went directly to their offices — there would be hours when the vast building was empty except for the attendants and grudging his energy he traced circles broken only by moments when the track stopped : his mean-ing gone, he waited for it to move again. The unspeakable boredom, and of the onlookers, poisoned the air more thoroughly than their breath and sweat. No one could have helped guessing that this boredom was the edge of a Gobi desert, that if nothing were done, if springs were not found quickly, the sand would cover everything, streets, homes, the lives of children. No simply human impulse would escape.

It was not for nothing that the painters in favour, on show in the many small galleries and the shops, all belonged to the avant-garde. Very much so. Like their open hatred of the present, their terror of a future they felt to be cruel and un-manageable drove them on farther and farther in their effort to out-distance it, to get beyond — feeling, sensation, life.

Stripped naked to the intellect, blind as it is, and often ulcered, they erected their scaffoldings of lines and spirals, round nothing. They had only to walk along the street to find, among the respectably ugly houses of which Berlin is full, one where their intellect was completed by forms of sensation as dry and as, emptily, perverted. . . . In a room more decently null than an A.B.C., young men in low-cut evening dress, rouged, eyebrows plucked, dance together with the decorum of schoolgirls : a girl comes on the tiny stage, her dress shows the length to the waist of a white back and childishly rounded knees ; as she dances she lifts thin arms. No, she is a young man — kept, they say, by the elderly gentleman at the next table. He looks like a distinguished civil servant or a banker : he has been reading until this moment — what ? — Rilke's *Sonette an Orpheus*. Really ? Does he hope that the poet will tell him how to tame beasts, or, perhaps, how to change what is only sterile to a young healthy child ?

For the simpler animal joys, there is the Bock-Bier-Fest in Neue Welt, and the tall building in which every floor is a different country ; for a few shillings the clerk and his girl travel from Spain to Turkey, and back through Vienna to dine on a terrace looking across the Danube. Synthetic travels, pains, joys — the place is crowded, but it is obvious as soon as you leave that some young men are not content. Outside, nailed on the bare trees of the street and on kiosks, posters accuse the Nazis of murdering so many Communists : Erich Kassner, baker, Johann Sieber, schoolboy — and the rest — quite thirty of them. At the other side of the same tree, the same kiosk, Nazi posters, with the list, not so long, of their dead. And in his usual place, hiding one of the posters, the man — not a beggar, no one in Berlin is allowed to beg — holding a copy of a magazine, always the same, with the photograph, mildewed, of a film star. He is silent : difficult not to think that his voice was long since frozen in him. The wind in these first months of the year in Berlin is bitter, made of particles of ice gathered on its way across the plains to the east ; they torment nerves and skin. He endures it, and the blackened snow under his feet, without moving, his back to the tree, upright in his working-man's jacket and thin trousers pulled in by the leather belt. It astonishes that he is neat, the long and deep hollows of his face shaved and clean. Misery, a misery formed from the lack of everything a living creature needs to hope, never kept itself cleaner. His skin has the grey surface of wax, his eyelids have become raw ulcers, his limbs bone, or gristle. He still, it seems, respects himself a little, enough to spend on keeping tidy what, if he put it in his mouth, would make a small difference in his hunger. The day when his self-respect fails, he will not begin to be filthy, he will kill himself — adding another to the daily self-murders of workless men. Why has he not joined one of the parties which at least clothe and feed their followers ? Perhaps the lists behind him are the answer. In that case he must also be scrupulous — or very simple. Perhaps he has really passed beyond, and if it exists at all in his cold thoughts, the future does not alarm him. He is simply waiting.

When I could, I avoided him. It needed more courage than I have, to look at him and realise that there are women who give birth only to hunger, to a lifelong defeat. He was a denial of all happiness, mine and others'. Denial without issue — unless, unless the future were not what, already, we expected and feared.

*

Do you remember the Germany — of our grandfathers, was it ? — of sentimental journeys to the Rhine, evenings of music, vows, and tobacco-smoke ? Did not your grandmother sing *At Ehren on the Rhine* ? It was still alive, that perhaps harmless Germany, in the over-furnished and shabby room where the elderly professor of music and his bouncing wife, both Prussians, were entertaining their friends : the old actress — her voice strong enough yet to declaim Schiller ; the young smiling Jew from the Spielhaus orchestra ; and the not very young woman who was still being given only maidservants to play, but she was studying, learning the whole of long parts, ready for anything, any ordeal, rather than give it up and return home. And how they enjoyed themselves, reciting, playing duets, running to the table to swallow another thin slice of leberwurst, slapping each other on the bottom, talking music, Schiller, Reinhardt, and laughing, laughing.

No one had told them they were a good seventy-five years out of their time, memories, not people. The future was in the universities, called Wartehalle für Unbeschäftigte, waiting-rooms for the workless : or — I had been listening to it that afternoon — it was a schoolboy of ten or eleven, eyes sparkling with anger, hands clenched.

"Listen to me," he cried, "Englishwoman — listen ! *We* did not sign that treaty. No, no, no, no, no ! We young ones say no."

*

Those years when my work — not then to write books — involved me in knowing a great many people, in being liked by them. Horrible years ! Horrible life ! My worst self had it entirely her own way. An acrobat, condemned to go through the same tricks, month after month, before the same indifferent faces, is not more uselessly agile. And it was my spirit I allowed to walk on its hands, to somersault, and develop smiles like knots of muscle.

I woke in the morning, for a single moment myself, Hervey Russell, and unhappy, because of all I was wasting, and not only of my own life. But the imposture had to go on — I thought, not having the courage or sanity to give it up — there were letters to write, making use of that mirror trick of the brain. You know it ? The words he is writing are reflected back on to the writer's mind from the future mind of the reader, and he has only to take them down. A trick it is only allowable to play for a good reason. All my reasons were poor : it was to satisfy an employer that I put myself in the posture of admiring what I detested ; soothing the vanity of a man who ought to have been told simply that he was a common fraud ; approaching humbly important persons who did not want to see me, and before whom, if my respect were real, I felt only an angry fatigue.

What more did I do that day ? Called on a publisher who kept me waiting an hour after the time of the appointment, and said genially, "I wonder why I asked you to come, I only deal

with the heads of firms, it saves so much misunderstanding " ;
listened for three hours, wearing the most amiable of masks,
to a novelist who must on no account be displeased, or in her
insolently virtuous way she will cheat us : after this interview,
when I was in the street, I discovered that in the labour of attention fragments of my mind had worked loose and fallen on
her floor ; impossible to go back ; besides, by this time they
had been swept up.

In the evening I have uninvited visitors : I approve eagerly
of opinions I despise, and betray by a cowardly silence others
I respect ; I join in praising an imbecile and allow a friend to
be severely judged ; to give pleasure to eight people, of whom
I like one, I make myself their lowest common factor and wear
anything they throw me, whether it is clean or not.

At last they go. My spirit — or what I take to be my spirit
— runs behind them for several moments, a dog which has
forgotten which of these strangers is his master. I open the
window, to feel the night on my face, but feel nothing — grown
part of my skin, the mask is still there, I take my hands to it,
but there is still another, and another, skin after flayed skin,
and I scarcely remember whether I have a face of my own or
not. Humiliated and vexed, I begin to prepare for bed. Now
I know that I shall never do anything which can justify me
for the lives I have sacrificed to come here. . . . A child is
perhaps crying. . . . If I could be sure who was crying, it
might be well to listen.

It is too late. Sleep.   *

Where I am living is very handsome, very fine, but it is not
my country. Every day I take a steep road up a hill, on either
side there are other hills, a valley, the sea — things, forms, that
encompassed my childhood, and for hundreds of years — and
not one of them has a voice I can hear. Endlessly I look at
absent hills ; their roads follow the threads of my nerves, and
day and night my nerves think of them. Yet it was here, in
my own country, from the country of my own nerves, began
my habit of running away. It began when I was a young girl.
Perhaps it is not wholly a bad thing for a writer to tear his

roots out of a ground where they cannot grow an inch without touching some memory which is either five or five hundred years old — five or five hundred, the words it uses are the same. It teaches him in time to send roots down in himself — if he has the energy : let us say, of a Rilke or a Valéry (French writers are peculiarly fortunate in that, born in a village, a province, they find it again intact in Paris : all France is the province of Frenchmen). But each time that I have run away — and from a habit it quickly became an illness — I have betrayed someone. Myself, but not always only myself.

*

Kneeling, looking into the fire, I am listening to my mother and another equally arrogant old woman. They are discussing the books — of household knowledge — and certain of them are very old, that they use. It is clear, though neither would admit it, that the books, which have been turned over by so many hands — what a family of hands ! mine scarcely seem to belong to me any more — use them, and impose habits, a gesture, which repeat themselves in the women of my family as often as my mother's coldly staring blue eyes and the boredom which seizes them in their thirties more brutally than the strokes from which, much later, they get their second and final death. With her customary firmness, my mother says, " It is always best to use the best " — (I recall a long dish on which, at the end of every week and again on Wednesday, pounds of yellow butter were set side by side on the stone shelf). Now and then they ask me, the young woman, with condescension, for an opinion, and I give it humbly.

A woman is working in a room which is indistinct because I cannot separate it from myself : outside, the air is fresh, with the freshness and clarity of a world emptier than ours. The light shock when the woman slips into my own body brings the two moments . . . not together, because there are no longer two, there is only one moment, endlessly present. It has gone, the woman has gone. I listen to the voices, springing directly from an unimaginable past, as though the old chairs, too, were using their latest owners. Older than that, the voices come from the ground, from the streets of this old port, from the wharf and sail-loft ; from the nothing, the absence of voices which is marked by the sea-pitted stones . . . master mariner, beloved husband of . . . wife of the above . . . daughter, died in infancy.

I begin to suspect that a woman has nothing more important than this slow labour of creation, carried out through children and houses. The gesture with which one generation guards the next is the movement, and the only time we see it clearly, of life itself. There are perhaps a few women, a very few, who should put first knowledge, or creation in one of the arts or in another form of construction ; and these ought possibly to deny themselves marriage, or at least child-bearing. I am sure that, except in these rare instances, rarer than we like to believe, nothing a woman adds to or puts in the place of her endless labour as roof-tree, as the light voice which comforts a child who has wakened to find the room full of night, is of great value. And to do this work well, she should as far as possible live a long time in one place. What sort of tree can you plant afresh every few years ?

*

Then why, if you always, even when you were denying it with the most bitter rage, knew this, did you so often run away ? Why, having one day gone back to your place, having settled yourself in a room where each time you looked up from your table you saw the pattern of your nerves traced out on the side of a hill and momently had the inconceivable joy of fitting outer to inner, why did you, after only a few years, three, or four, leave it again ? You knew, surely, that in leaving a quiet life and to live (for the fourth time) in London, where inevitably your acrobat self would be called on for its tricks, you were betraying the only one of your selves who should have been listened to. Then why ?

The interval of sanity, the brief lightning-flash of will, had come to an end. Another will was in control — scarcely to be called a will. My vice of restlessness, blind greed, demon of change, ambition. Leave this house, which demands as much attention as an exacting wife, and apart from a window and a view is not even agreeable. Go, go — take your doubts, your dryness, despair, confusion, hidden violence, and clear out.

During these years of tranquillity I had been learning a new fear — no doubt it was an old one, another of the abolished and ever-audible voices. The fear that, any moment now, I should come to an end, and — still living — die of a dry throat, dry veins, powerless, choked by lies, defeated. *L'acédia, maladie des moines*, is not invariably a sign of spiritual delicacy. (In Baudelaire it was ; he had neither the energy nor the coarseness of fibre to save himself from being destroyed by the hostility of a middle-class civilisation : with as much probity and severe delicacy of spirit, and with far greater vitality, Péguy was nearing exhaustion when the war came to turn him into a symbol.) In an ignorant and clumsy writer, it can be the effect of an even brief insight. What ! *that* meanness ! Those foolish noisy lies !

There were other things. I did not know how to live — as the world itself does not. A lout, and part of my world by my egoism and self-deception, I wanted peace and reached out my hand for violence. Was it my hand ? Or one of those that grope through the roots and touch me when I am passing ? But I should be in control. . . . I controlled nothing, none of my lives. At times when I was peaceably talking to one, the other would throttle it. Solitude — violence ; forethought — lies, day-dreams ; gentleness — blind egoism and greed : all the contraries in one cracked earthenware bowl. None of your fine glass, no transparent Chinese tea-cup, no pure gold or excellent goblet — a common bowl, but filled with a scalding bitter drink.

Very, now I come to think of it, like the tea brewed in those pots which in many kitchens in Yorkshire stand all day at the side of the stove.

There was a thick frost over the ground the January morning when I left, for good, that house, to go back to a society I could only live with by changing from self to self a dozen times a day — until they became so worn and soiled that they were unfit to wear. The frost covered the soil with a brittle web — but strong enough to resist the sun — in which leaves, small stones, water, a feather, were trapped. A shadow, of a low cloud, cut in half my hill, and the road broke off there, a severed nerve.

Nothing, I thought, has ended. You have only run away again. Your past is unfinished where you left it off. Without going back, you have no future. In my body every nerve protested against the agony of parting with those other nerves — which I could look at for a moment before they became a vague confusion and corruption in my mind. Why add to the continuous corruption of my life another which was avoidable ? What, poor fool, can you learn if you never sit still, if renouncing nothing you give away all ?

The sun and darkness of my hill, the freezing air — what courage it would need to begin there again. And indeed there would not be early enough. It would be imperative to go farther back. Back and back — to the first cowardice, the first seed of treachery, the first infinitely-celled fear. Too far — you must try to live without your future.

*

She went full of resentment to an appointment with her first husband, not their first meeting since the divorce, but the first for several years. How could she not dislike him ? — he had been part, with his lies and folly, of her unhappiness for ten years, and she had injured him. But when she saw him she felt pity, and some other emotion which was, perhaps, only remorse, and pity for herself. Listening, as she had often listened, to his ready tongue, she prayed that just one of his plans might come off.

Of their life together the essence had escaped ; there was nothing. There was nothing even of the mud in which they sank. Only was left, a bitter salt, the memory — not even that, but purely a dry useless loss — of youth and young energy. She could recall that there had been days when to dream was as satisfying and fruitful as an act, but not a single moment of one of those dreams. That such unhappiness and joy had ended in nothing, unless in this absence, was unendurable. It defeated her and she felt already old. To say, in hope of consolation, that every person carries in him a great many deaths, and that what she felt was one death, evaded the insistent question, the only one. What had their life together made, that existed ?

A child, yes — but that child himself was another cause of cold-ness and division.

What have I that I can smile at ? she thought. Her unhappi-ness, the quarrels, had destroyed her self-confidence — if it had ever existed and was not wholly a young arrogance, built on first puerile success at a university. And had fed in her a grudg-ing instinct not to waste kindness on an object considered un-worthy. This surely was absolute failure. If one cannot love what is or seems worthless, it is because warmth and the power to love are not there.

But who, very young, knows that without having been taught ? Only the good or very simple. Certainly not a young woman by nature greedy, possessive, ignorantly ambitious. His mother had once said to her, " He is very young." But this she did not understand. To her, even younger, the words meant nothing.

She could not overlook his infidelity. Her vanity was in agony. She was destroyed in her own eyes. So much of our unhappiness is lived in by our memory, turning the knife on itself, that it was her childhood, listening to her mother's strong voice (" You are the laughing-stock of the neighbourhood "), which grimaced and said, ashamed : Everything is spoiled ; I should have been admired more than all, I should have been all ; if I am not all I am nothing. So, and for a long time, she was nothing, she was a resentment, breaking down in tears so corrosive that in the end they burned away even her feeling of disgrace. Everything : except her self-pity. Then she wanted to go away, but a nerve still joined her to him, and he was able, by drawing his too articulate emotions across it, to make her feel that she was guilty of cruelty. She wept again. Would she have gone if, as anyone coming back to life from an illness strengthens his weak thread of new-born life by fastening it to the tree under his window, she had not turned to another her blind will ?

Her feeling of guilt was far heavier than the sin of abandon-ing him. It seemed the whole of her being. At this moment he took all, all the blame. But this, too, was a lie — a mask it on to avoid seeing her own face. It is true, she thought, that partly our failure had to do with my passion to be in the right. Which involves wanting other people to be wrong. Worse — to be pointed at as wrong. How often had she betrayed him by speaking of his cruelties, lies, ugliness, and disguising her own ? But — strip off all these masks, you will not even then find innocence. No, no, her guilt sprang far deeper than any harm she did him.

They had nothing to say to each other now. With relief, she hurried away from him, to go home. She was oppressed by the nothing of their marriage. Suddenly, with excitement, almost joy, she reflected that what had been made, and endlessly, was the single impact of two youthfully irreconcilable energies, already, when they met, turning away from each other. But the instant of meeting, which existed only in the past, was real — as though a word were the equal of all the silence that precedes and follows it — and indestructible : two streams rushing down hill touch, and for a moment before dashing separately aside, widely separate, on their way to the lower valleys, form a deep pool. It existed in them now as a denial. A stone had dropped out of sight in the pool, leaving only the spreading circles. They too had ceased. But accept, without bitterness, that they existed, exist, will always exist, in the being of the pool itself. It is the without bitterness that is important. Guilt . . . if she could accept, truly accept, even that, without distortion or exaggeration, she might hope one day to see the light which was so far behind her, and far, far behind the sun lying on the hill-sides of infancy. And, perhaps, so far ahead.

*

My mother stubbornly wanted perfection in the things round her. With only a little money to spend, she bought handsome old pieces of furniture, fine china, rugs. One afternoon she was standing close to a window examining a glazed bowl she held in both hands. Her latest find, it was beautiful ; in the glaze a great many flowers and small animals were gently reflected, as though they caught the sun. The artist must have watched in a mirror a long time before copying them. My mother looked at one, then at the next, and the next, with the inter-

gravity of a child. When I opened the door, she started and dropped the bowl. It broke on the polished floor into hundreds of pieces. The blood sprang to her face. Looking at me with a hotly fierce anger, she cried out,

" You fool. See, you've made me break it. Get away out of my sight. Go, go."

I fled : and carried my half-accepted guilt with me all day under the weight of her refusal to speak to me. Only in the evening when I was going up to bed, she said — it was as though the words jetted in her from a deep bitterness and grief — " No, if you hadn't come in I should never have dropped it. I couldn't. I never drop anything. Never, never, never."

*

The years when, living in London for the third time, I learned my acrobat's tricks, were not the lowest. That can be said of the two years immediately after the last war. Who recalls those years clearly ? The young dead were still so close that had we taken the trouble to listen their voices would certainly have carried back to us. Or we should have seen them, pointing out to one another something we overlooked, the early light, the pattern of foam between breaking waves, a hill carrying a house, things as common as these. A few of their contemporaries, among them poets, did listen. I did not. My energy in those days was inexhaustible, and I wasted it. Get, get, was all I heard. Things I despised — no, not despised, but denied — were waiting anywhere but in London for me to notice them. To my restless greed, they were as if lying at the other side of the grave. I wanted what I saw here. I bought — clothes, more than I needed, and too expensive ; pieces of furniture, old and again costly, for a house I had no intention at present of living in : to get a lacquered tallboy I coveted, I borrowed money and began a series of debts. In the hours when I was not working for a firm of advertisers, I did not read, nor try even to think. I was a greedy gaping mouth for the cheapest and easiest sensa-ions.

In my firm, we dealt in lies. Advertising is that — even those rms of it worked out by otherwise decently intelligent men

— the skilful use of the truth to mislead, to spoil, to debase. It is true we were servants, not masters. But through us, as much as through newspapers and books, the greater part of its truth was sucked from life ; sham needs were forced into it. We are still chewing the sour kernel, without the courage to spit it out. I was bored by my work in this place, and without much conscience revolted by its futility : my boredom spilled over into the evenings I emptied out in the least intelligent ways, like an animal, without the animal's pure pleasure in living.

To think of the time I wasted — and if it had been only time ! What did I not waste of a swiftly-passing present, of a child's first gestures to the world, of tranquillity, of a truth which then slipped out of my reach, never to be seen again in my life. Sometimes now I remember to be thankful to have been spared a severer punishment than the one I gave myself, I who could not wait for anything, imprisoned in my impatient greed. Who did not even imagine what to ask for.

Why did no one, not one person, turn me round at that time and order me to look at myself ? But no one has the right to be saved from outside, by another hand.

Years later, reading Alain-Fournier's ironically romantic book, I came on a passage which conveys wholly one aspect, the innocent, of those years : *c'est la ville déserte, ton amour perdu, la nuit interminable, l'été, la fièvre. . . .*

Yes, certainly a fever — but in life there are no victims, except among very young children. We others *catch* our illnesses, we run after them and insist upon succumbing — and afterwards excuse ourselves and complain of our sufferings. The strangest thing about life is not its frightful cruelty, but that it can be gentle.

*

Yet I had a chance to see myself. A mirror was held up to me two or three times by a life precisely the opposite of mine, truthful where mine was a sham, as clear as mine was stained and confused.

By some kindness I was taken to Walter de la Mare's house at Anerley, for a Sunday afternoon and evening, the day when his friends visited him. Afterwards I went again — twice three times ? — always afraid to be unwanted if I went too often. You took the train through several stations, then a tram, to reach an almost country street of quiet houses, each with its garden at the back. It was indubitably not country, yet was not urban ; it held itself in a gently grave space between them, and contented. I recall little of the inside of the house, except a polished table and the bowl in which raspberries, currants, and cherries drowned in their thick juice. It was, perhaps, an ordinary enough house, such as a French poet might have lived and worked in for years, as in the too great lucidity of his mind. There was more here, in this house and its small garden — secluded as only in an English street the gardens can be — than light ; there were children and their quietly-smiling mother ; there was an order and friendliness of material things. Enclosing all, yet in its place as an unexacting part of all, the preoccupations, disinterested, of Walter de la Mare himself. Even I grasped the relation between the friendly and allusive ease of these conversations, and a poetry which has the brightness, the purity, the ambiguous depth of pools in which a river is lost. Even I could not avoid noticing that part, perhaps the greater part, of the intimacy and light seriousness of the talk was due to the one of his qualities only to be pinned down as absence. He did not live in the same world with us. He was present, blowing a simple idea into fantastic shapes, deflecting any lack of charity (not once did I hear him even think a malicious comment), listening to all the others, ready when no one else chose to speak to lift into daylight a web of analogies, like an anatomist laying open a network of nerves — but his analogies were taking part in a ballet — and not present, politely absent in a solitude which assumed him, not he it. Even I could see that as all this was outside — a singular probity, the fine essence of friendliness, detached attentive curiosity towards the nature of events (all : in nature and in the mind), an irony not weighted by malice, the impossibility of a false or awkward use of words or the spirit — so it was inside. The atmosphere of the house was only these turned inside out, and simple. No faintest hint of the cenacle about these Sunday evenings, nor of the salon. A garden behind a rather small suburban house, and a room, easily approachable, one of the only two perfect examples of hospitality I have known — because centred on itself although open to all the possibilities of thought.

Why did I not see that I was being shown the pattern of a truthful life ? Blinded by what thick gross flesh, which let me see and not see, admire without learning, and return, as if drugged, to my mental and emotional squalor ?

Who now lives in that house ? They inherited a fortune unless, like me, they were too dense to pick it up.

That year, solemnly, I took one of the folders we used in the office and wrote on it : Letters from Famous Men. Years later I found it at the bottom of a trunk. It contained two brief friendly notes from Walter de la Mare.

*

What had I left, to live my distracted and sterile life ? Nothing. No one except a child not yet four.

I want to act justly towards my young self. It is easy for me to overwhelm her with reproaches, to abuse her. To her is due my most piercing regret ; to her restlessness, her horror of a settled life, her puerile ambitions. The error she made was capital. Its guilt is the heaviest of all those I carry, and irredeemable ; I cannot accept it, as I can my other failures. The temptation to treat her as an enemy, a criminal, or more simply a fool, is very great. But let us listen to any excuses she has to offer. Her youth ? Her curiosity, the greedy violence of the life given to her ? Her wish to prove that she was not, in the worldly sense, a failure, not, by her mother to be written off as a disappointment, merely a married daughter ? Why did she never think of all those youthfully-dead to whom nothing now was permitted, although doubtless they would have been pleased with what of life she was throwing aside ? Yes, why ?

But what use are these accusations ? She would say that she was driven. By whom ?

The sensible reasons she gave — that nothing much was to be expected of her husband, that it was on her their child depended for a satisfying future — only so many eddies above the secretly strong under-current. It swept her away from what for nearly four years had been the deep centre of her life, when she was drudge to a small house, servant to her child and absorbed in serving him. To it she remained fastened by innumerable living threads. The room she rented in London had to be shared with the agony that seized her when she thought of him — at night, or at the hours when she would have been giving him his bath or in the early morning lifting him out of bed. Her mother wrote to her that on the first morning when his kind foster-mother went in, he sat up in bed and said quickly, as if propitiating her, " Good-morning." She cried as she had never cried, and knocked her blind head on the wall. Night after night. . . . Years later, when the child disappeared in a boy and a young man, words glossed over at the time — as if there would still be time to put it right — sprang awake, with a terrible freshness and power, to teach her the meaning of anguish. . . .

Time and again, driven by what hunger, she went back and lived with him in one place and another — for a few months or a year. In the long quarrel between her two hungers, time passed. At last it was too late. Only then she knew what she had been doing.

The other day I asked her why she had not been afraid to leave him.

" Did you never think he might die ? "

" No," she said instantly. " And later, when he was ill, I was there to nurse him. I should always have gone back for that."

Because at that time her own life was so strong in her, she had, I suppose, then, no fear of death.

*

Really there is no reason why childless people should have houses. One large room would be enough for each of us. Earlier in this war, when I reflected that at the end of it I must find a decent house to live in for the rest of my life, the thought pricked me that I had no child to keep in it.

How thankful I was to leave the first house I had. The difficulties I should face, living in other people's houses with a very young child, were nothing. I did not think of them ; I simply went, seizing the first chance to leave a life and a provincial city I detested. This, not the first stage of my journey, was the first time I ran away. Not my first serious blunder, it may have been the first fatal one. Childless people may drift as they please and, free of the intolerable burden of a house, adorn their shells with any charming or splendid pattern they can : a child needs solid earth for his roots. Deprived of it, he is led to look for it in himself. The process is a dangerous one : if it turns out well, what has been lost? Nothing—only the past.

When I went into that house, I knew — knew, I say — that the trap had closed ; I was caught by everything I had determined to avoid, possessions, a settled life — and the repetitive drudgery, distractions, forethought, involved in looking after a house. I hid, as I thought, my increasing anger. It gave me away one evening when I wanted to put off the moment of going in. My mother was there, and scolded me as if I were still a child. Did she at that moment forget her own boredom when she was younger ? It was a disease which attacked her like an animal. It broke out in terrifying fits of rage, in which she slammed the doors of her room again and again, and at last locked herself in there with it for hours. I would prepare a tea-tray with the intense anxiety a child is able to feel but not to see the end of, and take it up. Setting it on the floor, I knocked. " I've brought you your tea." No answer. Sometimes I crept away, leaving the tray. At others I waited, sitting mutely on the top stair, for an hour, hours, long after the tea had become cold and useless. These rages, inexplicable at the time, a cyclone which blew up and devastated our lives, bewildering us, until it wore itself out and dropped — only later I began to realise that they had been boredom, a violent boredom, and a despair equal to it, which had no outlet except this useless one. What child could have helped her ? A little later, I must still have been very young, I learned to feel less anxious. The anxiety was there, stupefying me a little, but I went on blindly with whatever I was doing. One day she said to me in a curious voice, " You have no milk of human kindness." It was after one of these storms, and I had left her alone for hours, while I sat and painted in the kitchen, not thinking about her.

Don't you see that I had not understood? That a child could not, without more help?

*

The turning-points of a life can be seen long after. A traveller on foot climbs hill after hill, always in front of him another, not aware that he has ceased to climb and is avoiding the more difficult paths. One day, turning his head, he finds himself opposite a gap in the hills, which are closing behind him. On the horizon, he sees it was there he turned off. Impossible to think of going back ; his feet are heavy with the earth he has been walking in, he cannot climb even the nearest hill : he cannot even imagine what the country was really like — were there frosts, and days of chill discouragement, rain coming through your shoes, and cracks opening in the ends of your fingers? Viewed from here, it lies in a delicious serenity, warm, the tops of trees inviting to sleep. The thought occurs to him — or is it a memory? — that at one time, when he was looking forward, he saw this serenity in front of him :

> *Et les premiers jouets de la jeune lumière*
> *Iles ! . . . Ruches bientôt quand la flamme première*
> *Fera que votre roche, îles que je prédis,*
> *Ressente en rougissant de puissants paradis,*
> *Cimes qu'un feu féconde à peine intimidées,*
> *Bois qui bourdonnerez de bêtes et d'idées. . . .*

Some time early in 1914, Harriet Shaw Weaver offered me two pounds a week — it was her own money ; and the journal she edited, which was publishing *Ulysses* at the time, must have been costing her much heavier sums — so that I could come to London. Where had I met her? It must have been the year before, when I was for the first time in London, living in the greatest poverty and happiness, and writing, for my Master's degree, with all the impudence in the world, a thesis on European drama. She was generous and disinterested to a degree scarcely conceivable in the world of letters. The delicacy of her offer to a student, a girl of whom nothing was known ; there was nothing to know — did I thank her suitably for it? I must have done my best.

I accepted. But, a day or two later, I wrote again, refusing. That I was leaving her made my mother very unhappy, and this time I had not the courage, or harshness, to insist on going. Imagine : if I had gone to London then and worked on *The Egoist*, I should have met and listened to those few writers who were bringing disgrace on themselves by writing as though there were still something fresh to say about man and his nature, and new ways of saying it — new at least in England. Uncouth as I was, a lettered barbarian, but full of curiosity, and perhaps teachable, I could not have helped learning a little. And I should have stayed in London, with them, not put myself in the power of one person. Everything would have gone otherwise than it did. Might I not even have learned to write ? Instead of pouring out — first in a blind gross impulse (I could not look truthfully at a single object, still less at myself) ; then, when I had created for myself imperative needs and must have money for them — a number of silly and meaningless books ? It must be said, too, that I had no idea they were without meaning. Perhaps, after all, I was unteachable. . . .

*

When for the first time a human being was able to separate himself from an object — animal or idea — and so to re-invent it, why had he an impulse to paint it on the wall of a cave or make a song of it ? Why was he not content simply to embrace it with his thoughts ? It was perhaps because he was a failure in other ways : not a clever hunter, he impressed himself on the men he despised with their invariable luck as bores, by drawing the horses they tamed and the bears they killed ; or he was blind and sang to prove how brightly he saw. . . . With the achievement of happiness for all, there may be no artists. All will be content simply to live, with grace, energy, reason ; and when they are old, to sit still. What a magnificent world ! What harmony ! . . . There are no signs of it.

*

It is perhaps an exaggeration — but one of those by which children who are lying tell more of the truth — to say that what drew me to study European dramatists (in place of the anodyne theme given me by my professors) was a vague notion that drama, more clearly than any of the other arts, even than music, offers the analogy of a universal art — or act — of creation. There was much talk then, in the year before the first war, about the Theatre. Without excuse, I formed an idea of the Theatre which had no relation, or the vaguest, with the theatre as it was. And this idea — of a stage or temple where, between the actors' gestures and the imagination of the dramatist, the myths governing man's thoughts and through them his acts, would be given a form — haunted me during the year and a half when day after day I sat and read the plays of modern dramatists. Half aware of it, I expected to find, here or in some other country, a drama which evoked in the spectators their creative impulse, so that it was an action taking place in themselves, a discovery of their own emotions and development of their own thought, which was made visible on the stage.

After two or three disappointments I did not go to the theatre. I had so little money. It was too vexing to spend it on watching through an evening the succession of trivial events or an intrigue, which fell about the stage like lumps of plaster from a ceiling and was supposed to have something to do with life. To the totality of the thoughts and feeling of our time, it bore the same relation as to the body one of its dry nail-filings. The real interest of the theatre was the audience, as I saw it from pit or gallery — a monster, part animal, part God, simultaneously living and dying, covered with eyes, a brain over which the dramatist's needle was moving without starting up a single coherent phrase ; but the creature was alive, born every instant in the bubble blown by the lights, and dying as many deaths. Here, and behind my eyes, and not on the stage, was solved that problem of simultaneity which haunts every writer — and can only be solved by suggestion, never by logical statement.

Walking every day from my room to the British Museum : there to sit reading and, with a ruthlessness not yet twenty years tired, condemning printed play after play : when I glanced up, or when the closing bell went, it was a shock to find myself shut in by the circles of books and the dome : dizzy from it, and sometimes a little from having eaten nothing since break-fast, I wandered out into the hall, to feel the walls still pressing me and the insistent unreality of the statues, and so into daylight or dusk, the pigeons tumbling under their stone ledge, the side-streets opening books and buttered crumpets in their windows, a sky heavy with sunset, the creases of the monster's brain, unintelligible, turning with the axles of the street and the angles of house-fronts and gutters.

Better than the theatre was to spend sixpence on a seat in the gallery of the Coliseum. It was there I saw a Reinhardt ballet, my first ballet, and though I think it was only clumsily exotic it proved to me that I had been right to stay away from the theatre. It was a revelation of what can be evoked, what underworlds of insight and feeling brought together into the daylight (or the light from the immense candelabra of the scene). The music created its own space, in which dancers and spectators could move freely, and simultaneously time was creating itself in the movements of the dancers, the memory of one gesture reflected in all those nearest it. A whole, a poem formed by the enclosing definite acts of the music and the indefinite continuously unfolding gestures of the dance, was becoming. Willingly or unwillingly, the spectator re-lived the action end-lessly evoked in himself and the universe, the upward spring, the instant, imperceptible, of arrest, the descent, and again the spring. What was development in the single dancer became in the whole ballet the idea itself of movement — that is, of life.

And then to leave the theatre and walk home, with one of the friends of that time (God be thanked, of this, too), through London streets not yet spoiled by too powerful lights. The emptiness of our stomachs was scarcely even an inconvenience. We had the future to feed on. And at present we had the dark streets leading to the river, and the river itself, concealing light below its cracked surface (concealing, if we had known it, terror and conflagrations), and our talk, endless, like the river, like the ballet, like our lives. These were months of freedom from responsibilities not begun in dreams. We were indifferent, being so young, to the lower-middle-class world in which our poverty forced us to live. Why should we who had just enough to eat, our country eyes, music amiably free of charge (or almost), the post-Impressionists, and had discovered Anatole France, mind ?

I was free. No one obliged me to consider him, to love or be loved. Whatever I took in my hand, a fine morning or a book, could absorb me : I had not to wonder whether something else or some person were being robbed. In some way, and without being able to pay the price asked for it, I have been looking ever since for a freedom of this order.

*

Yes, freedom — but already illusory. Before this, at the university, I had involved myself in obligations and lies. I was only putting off the moment when they would fall due. . . .

The first accident shaping my life was that I went, instead of to one of the older universities, with a formal discipline, to Leeds. No one except those who are touched by it in youth, understands the nostalgia of the industrial North. They only can play on the keyboard stretching from deep valleys, smooth grey hills or roughened with bracken, moor, to slate roofs, stone, cobbled streets slippery with soot, the hard cold husk of a sound kernel. Indescribable in a phrase, the smoky sunlight which a northerner returning home feels as warm on his skeleton as the sun of the Midi. The silence in mid-afternoon, in one of the villages where every man and almost all the women are at work in the mill, is like and entirely unlike the silence of a French village. On a day of wind, sun, and cloud, the air here is thin and strong, marking out the stone, soot-blackened, of the houses, the stream running discoloured past the mill, and the clear smaller stream running to join it : the life here — it derives only from the eighteenth century — has the toughness of the far older life of the French village ; it is cruder, less civilised, less rich ; it has less imagination and less cruelty : it is unlikely to breed a poet or a monster, admired, of rapacity. We are average people, we northerners, not lacking, though, in salt. And we are restless. Restlessness which drives a man out of his valley is not French.

A harshness, a sense of urgency, penetrated me through the

distractions I found here or made for myself. They sharpened my anxiety to do well. The responsibility, after all, was mine. It was I who had said first that a university was the next stage : it had been understood for a year that I was working for a scholarship. But at the last, and when I was getting ready, my mother began to be afraid of the future and sad. Gold mesh purses were very fashionable in those days : with what money I had to spend I bought one for her " to take shopping ".

" It won't comfort me in my lonely round," she said seriously.

Without trying to, I shut away the part of my mind which a phrase of this sort could stab. I must go. A year at the Municipal School in Scarborough — I lived during the week in rooms, with a landlady indifferent to my comings and goings, and believed that now I was self-reliant ; in many ways I was more ignorant than a child, and intractable when I feared being laughed at — had stirred a thick ferment in me. Rising in my veins and behind my eyes, it blinded me to everything except my intense need to get away.

When I left she travelled with me as far as Scarborough. Standing on the platform, she looked up at what must have been my carelessly eager face. If I could see her. But there is only a pale shadow. The image which comes if I persist, has the unreal smoothness of a photograph. It is a photograph, of that time. An assassin of memory. I am sorry that photographs were invented. They are infinitely worse than nothing.

Then she must have walked away alone, to go through what of the ritual of a day in Scarborough she had courage for.

*

Dresse-toi nu, vaillant ; fais craquer les gaînes ; écarte de toi les tuteurs ; pour croître droit tu n'as plus besoin que de l'élan de ta sève et que de l'appel du soleil. I came on this and copied it — some years ago, but already too late to be of any use. And I doubt whether the advice, although offered by one of the most distinguished of living writers, would help anyone except a person who did not need it. How well I understand now the changes of corruption in a young soul ! At first everything calls it —

things, the faces of strangers, even the uncouth streets of an English industrial city. An uncontrolled excitement rises through the body : in the veins, and the spaces round the heart, the pressure very soon becomes more than the soul can bear ; scarcely able to breathe, it lets the body rush it out of the library where it ought to be working, absorbing knowledge — anywhere, to the tennis courts, the refectory, the corridors, where it may catch glimpses of magnificent young men on their way to lectures or laboratories, even to the ugly city, to cafés and bookshops. This immature soul has no ballast to keep it from rolling in the lightest swell starting from a malicious object. And where it runs aground it is caught : nothing now can save it from the assault of those strong tropical-seeming plants which push everywhere their fleshy stems. A storm only will free it, and at what cost.

In my lodging, I am working late — to make up for time wasted during the day. The gas hisses behind a yellow globe, the old wall creaks. Suddenly, in the silent street, footsteps, or someone cries out in the next room, in his sleep — the engineering student who took the room yesterday and tomorrow on the stairs will rush past me, late for a lecture : the footsteps die away, the sleeper turns over (no doubt his bed is no less hard and ridged than mine), but my mind has been wrenched out of the book it with reluctance had drawn round itself, it is already a vapour, or it dreams, dreams foolish or childishly obscene, which cripple it for living.

Nothing, neither the harshness often of my upbringing, nor my ambitions, had disciplined me. I was helplessly the servant of my senses. The reproofs, mild and half-amused, of senior students, strengthened in me only distrust and the hatred I felt for authority. A fairly stable rock was my ambition, but a rock the foam hid.

In the end I passed out at the head of the Honours list in my subject. No more ignorant and undiscriminating mind ever played the examinations cards with more spirit.

*

Once it was only books which forced us to think about

cruelty, *homo homini lupus*. The incautious pages let slip tortured limbs of mediaeval peasants, criminals broken on the wheel, bodies of children and women lying under the charred beams. These memories, not or not entirely our own, have a trick of jumping out in the dark to strike. That can be dealt with. But when it starts up in our life, only next door, near enough for us to learn the stench of terror — no use closing our eyes, even no use pinching nostrils ; the smell of concentration camps is stronger even than the smell of blood running into the ground during a war. (Because of the air-raids, civilians are not, as they were in the last war, excited by this.)

An animal is not cruel ; it lives wholly in the instant leap on its prey, in the present taste of marrow or blood. Cruelty begins with the memory, and the pleasures of the memory are impure ; they draw their strength along levels where no sun has reached.

At last I am beginning to understand it. A trifling incident put me on the track. The other day I bought some toothpaste of a brand which so far as I knew at the moment I had never used. In the evening when I opened the tube a fine aromatic scent was set free, and at once I was in the long shadowy bathroom of the school I went to when I was ten or eleven. It was a private school, kept in a long house, shabby and handsome, near the harbour. From the upper schoolroom, you saw the gleaming nap of the harbour, the abandoned shipyards, the gulls. At the back a flagged yard, where we played a little. Tricked, the rooms and wide staircase and this yard gave themselves up to me, with a deceptive clarity and, clinging to them, as fresh as if it had done nothing all these years but lie in the earth, a memory I was too slow, and weaker than it, to escape. I was in the yard : other children, stretching the skipping-rope between them, were running round me to draw it tightly round my ankles. In a moment I should fall, helplessly bound, on the stone flags. I stood there, and showed none of my humiliation ; nor my fear. I remember walking away, a murderer in my will.

What smiled in their eyes when they tightened the rope and watched me was curiosity — they were exploring the nature of reality — but curiosity bearing a negative sign.

Cruelty is that — as, on the whole, science is the mind's positive
curiosity. Without cruelty, no evolution. In what fusion, and
final complete satisfaction, will evolution bite its tail, and curiosity, with cruelty, cease? Fortunate moment for man, and
his last.

*

This cannot have been my earliest practice in hiding marks
of fear or chagrin. One day I was in the street outside a shop.
How small I still was I can see by the low window-sill of the
shop, on a level with my head. The sixpence I was holding
slipped from my fingers, rolled, and fell through the grating
of a drain. Shock, the fear of my mother's anger, ran through
me, and at the same instant I thought that I should be laughed
at, and my face hardened in an unnatural calm. My terror now
was that I had been seen. And someone had seen, a benevolently
smiling woman.

" What did you lose? " She opened her purse.

" Nothing," I said.

" Oh, surely——? "

" Nothing." I walked away from her quickly, hot with
vexation that my loss had been noticed. Surely, under cover
of her interest, she was laughing?

*

From the time I could read, when I was four years old, I
read indiscriminately, and merged with myself all I read. I
recall infantile obscenities I drew out of a story of the Indian
Mutiny : and during a long time — how long I cannot now
judge — another I and the characters of various books were
living a romantic life in a country happily situated in my
stomach. Later I began to be punished for hiding books, so
that I could read as I dressed, under the mattress of my bed.
I must still have been very young, because I continued to hide
them in the same place, forgetting, between beatings, that they
would be discovered.

There were certain volumes of fairy-tales I read again and
ᵹain. Even then I guessed that the myth of the Younger
ʳother is older and more serious than the others. It seems, too,

that I may have understood it, in part. Only in part. I knew that one must leave the comfortable shadow thrown by the mother, or remain always poor and ridiculous. But nothing warned me that the whole past is stronger than her shadow, harder to escape from. That the energy of a lifetime cannot break the habit formed too early of walking — stumbling, rather — with eyes turned to the young daylight touching purely the nocturnal coasts of a childhood.

A story, *The King of the Yellow Dwarfs*, gave me a shock. It ends in the triumph of injustice, infinitely more terrifying than a cruel or sad tale. It is, I think, the only one. I would as soon leave an infant to play with a sharp knife as let him read this story before he is old enough to defend himself against it.

*

Six years old, or at most seven, I may have been when my mother went a long voyage without me — I think to the Argentine. She put me to live in the small dame's school next door, kept by two sisters. I recall that she promised me, before she went, if she died, to come and see me. But it was not fear of a ghost overcame me as soon as I was put to bed, and every night during the four months she was away : it was a dreadful anxiety and desire to see her. I implored her to come, if only for a moment. I cried and cried, and one of the sisters came upstairs to reason with me. But it was stronger than my terror of being scolded or pitied. Nothing, until sudden sleep came, was any good.

The next long voyage she went, a year or two later, I was indifferent. But on the last morning I made a pretence of being sad. I knew she expected it.

Already I felt my responsibility for her happiness. Why ? It was not that, were she disappointed or bored, her children would vex her — which meant a thrashing : with good reason we feared our thrashings. No — it came, I am certain, from a knot tied in one of my nerves when I was born, to remind me that I must do something about her disappointment. How far I was from understanding its depth, and lifelong and inappeasable bitterness . . . yet my anxiety to please her had the compulsic

of pity : it was a little too large for me. If she were unhappy
I felt instinctively guilt, not fear. A picnic where something
happened which amused her gave me a delicate feeling of
triumph. Did she find a common wild flower and ask me what
it was called ? — it was, I told her, very rare here. The sky
clouded over for rain ? As we walked, I pushed the clouds
back with my will.

You could think I had an ear growing inside hers, a pulse of
mine in her wrist.

One day she was dressing to go out. I asked when she was
coming back. " Never," she said, with a bitter slowness. She
was vexed with my father. In their quarrels she could not
make a reconciling gesture ; it must come from him and be
made more than once before her strong pride, really disappointment, was appeased. (I was always hers — and yet, since I
cannot easily hurt anyone's feelings, I talked to him when she
could not hear me.) Did I believe she meant this ? Enough to
follow her when she left the house. We walked a mile or so
into the country, I a hundred yards behind, just out of sight,
I thought. There was sunlight between the strong shadows of
trees. She stopped and looked round : when I reached her she
ordered me — I suppose gently, since I was not afraid — to go
home. Did I obey her ? — I was hot and tired. And was
it then she turned back ? I can't remember. I see her only
in the moment when she turned her head and looked at me
coming behind her.

*

A port is a ship which has grown into the land. The waves,
striking its cliffs, its wharves, send a light trembling, unseen but
not unfelt, through the old streets. In the air, salt — and that
brightness reflected in a shower of rays from the sea, as though
a fish leaped and flashed past your eyes everywhere you glanced.
Gardens, houses, thoughts, turn away from the land, towards
flight. Among those living in any street, some have just returned
from Callao, Shanghai, Odessa, or that strange land known to
my infancy by the two names of Bonnus-Airs and The Plate ;
others are leaving again tomorrow. Of this one you are told :
last heard of in the perpetual night of Archangel in winter, his

ship frozen in the ice : a ship still free spoke him on her way home and heard that the captain had had his hand amputated after frost-bite : all winter his wife lives with this absence of a hand, but when light frees the other ships his has vanished ; nothing heard, nothing seen, of the moment when the ice broke in on her ; the darkness of the north has taken all. Of this young woman : her husband died of fever in Pernambuco. Of that old silent couple : when she was on a voyage with him, the ship barely lived through a hurricane : ask her — she has forgotten it. . . . The captain's wife, for whom foreign countries are only a coast-line and harbours, who has learned to live at ease in a cabin and endure the boredom of long voyages in a small steamer, is here and absent : she has her children and her house or she has her husband — rarely all three. There runs, through the quietest, least unconventional of homes, a current always of change, uncertainty, the thought and desire of voyages.

Every Victorian bracket and old cupboard of our house was filled with exotic fragments, fetched up here from the other side of the world — the side towards which, whether she had willed it or not, my mother's deepest nature was set — egg-shell china from Shanghai, the model, in scented wood, of a Chinese house, silks and etchings on copper from Sasebo, books printed in Tokio, hand-painted and fastened by a tiny ivory slipper, the huge seeds of tropical plants, fans, Spanish trays from Montevideo, lace and a shell from Tenerife. When she was very young my mother was bored by living at home. And I think her children bored her then.

She took me with her on voyages before I was old enough to bring back anything but a confused shifting brightness, colours, sounds ; they vibrate in my life as the sea through the air and earth of that port where I, fortunate, was born. There is always a sea breeze in my memory, but from what sea it comes who can be sure ? Not I. The salt touched my bones very early with its savour of other countries. A savour or a poison ? It scarcely matters. Who ever came home without he had first sailed ?

*

There were days, weeks, during the years before this war

when its journey brought it to the top of a hill and we could watch it crossing the stretches of high ground. Then the road dipped again into a defile. Had it, perhaps, decided to turn off along a side road or, changing its mind entirely, to turn back ? But irregularly, at increasingly short intervals, it reappeared. It was possible after a time to see its face and speculate on the time — months or years — it would take to reach us. A good many people, not all of them foolish or insincere — quite sincerely they deceived themselves and others — were not interested, and nothing irritated these more than to be seized, their arms shaken, and made to look at the road and that figure drawing week by week nearer. Either they smiled and said, " You are hysterical, my poor friend " — or, with impatience, " Nonsense. Don't you see that he is not looking this way ? Quite obviously he's turning east." Even when at his next and closer appearance the traveller was openly facing in our direction, they persisted in thinking that the road did not reach so far as us : it stopped some distance away, at a country and a people of whom we knew nothing. . . . In all countries a few men and women had persuaded themselves that the approaching figure was a friend. . . .

The mother of a son almost war age cannot persuade herself not to fear. . . . None of the three or four people with her in the room were able, except at moments, to deceive themselves. The length of their sight gave them no least pleasure : what they saw alarmed them ; and they were ashamed of their impotence. The League Council was in session at St. James's Palace, debating the German march into the Rhineland. To the onlookers, the Council offered the spectacle, odd if it had not been senseless and horrible, of a play acted by ventriloquist dolls, almost life-size, not the tenants of their words, able to fold their hands while turning their heads round in the full circle : in this posture, they mimed a Concert of Europe which left nothing to be imagined except the harmonies : their masks, still more their voices, were familiar : less informed people had been listening for years to these same voices exhorting, soothing, explaining, about the traveller, so many contradictory things that they had lost faith. Either the masks were lying or they were lamentably mistaken. Or because of some defect in their mechanism they had lost the power to make decisions. Some perhaps were already hopeless, others were self-assured and not without sympathy for the traveller ; others, again, were becoming desperate. They quarrelled. One, it is said, wept.

The real spectacle was not, perhaps, the one presented to the public : it was being rehearsed in the myopic heads behind the masks — or elsewhere.

" Is it possible," she asked, " that we are going to ally ourselves with Germany ? "

A soldier of the last war — he was thinking, no doubt, of that country of cemeteries which is northern France ; of the botched villages, of the thistledown touching the ear with a word spoken by any one of a thousand or so ghosts left to share the place with its few overworked inhabitants ; of the sunken scar in the wheat marking a trench — stammered, " If that happens, I shall enlist in the French army."

" And you expect the French to say thank-you for your offer ! "

" All that is charming," she said to him, " but I can't help feeling that a little common sense now would be more use." She was thinking : If our son were a child I could take him away, out of their reach. Herod may kill all the others, but mine would be safe. Unfair ? If it were possible to save one child out of twenty millions, would anyone for a moment hesitate ? Certainly not his mother.

" They always behave in exactly the same way, the dear Boches. They have learned nothing and they know nothing."

" Except about war."

" And music."

" Music to them is what their cathedrals are to the French — superb buildings, marvellous conquests of space, which seem to express the soul of the nation, and are only that soul's excuse for an inhumanity growing up outside. A German goes in and out of his music without giving it time to change his life."

" Yes, but if there is going to be war — when ? "

" In two years — at most three."

" What do you base that on ? "

" Listen——"

There is no need to listen. In the first place she had known
it since a day twelve or more years since, during a child's diphtheria
illness. She sat and watched him, in the weak circle of the night-
light, asleep, and easily. A thing happened which was not for
the first time — the image of herself became indistinct, merged
in that of the clumsy schoolgirl still conscious in her, then in
a crowd, indistinct, and as it were suppliant. A woman separated
herself from it, and became distinct — less her features than the
curve itself of her body and its cold. She stooped, outside the
smouldering door-beams of a house, a poor house, over a child's
dead naked body. It had been thrown down on stones his blood
made wet. None of this was a thought ; it was an experience
— of reality or of a reality ; and whether in the past or the
present did not arise. There was one, not two moments, an
absence, it could be, of time, confused with this double anguish ;
one cruelty — of life ; one rigidity of despair, which possessed
all her senses. A movement made by the living child in his
sleep brought her back — to inhabit the sole narrow island of
her mind which she could measure, which her strength equalled.
It was then, yes, when there were no present signs of a war,
that she began to fear one. Within a few years there were too
many and clear signs. The habits of rational speculation, of
questioning people, of collecting for its own sake information,
did not abolish the signs her self made to itself — as the afternoon
two years ago, when a cloudily bright sky thundered without
warning, a long clattering fearful peal : the trees started with
birds ; and she ran terrified to the window, certain — he was
away learning to fly — that he must have fallen with his aeroplane. And there were many nights when, the rest of her
household asleep, she walked in her room, and thought : I am
an old woman walking about an empty house ; I am defeated
now, I am nothing.

It was not only to make up to him, for everything, that she
spent on training him for life the greater part of all she had. It
was because of the war.

The voices crossed each other in the room in a growing
tension. It became harder to see who was speaking. Some of

the lighter voices might come from outside, from the waiting houses, or from any moment of the past or future. So few years separated these speakers from the young men they knew during the last war and who could not possibly, before they were silenced, have said all they had to say. Fewer still from the dead of the next.

" Surely it's time for the news ? "

She turned on the wireless. A voice flowed like slightly rancid oil through the room. . . . *S O S. I'm falling. Oo-oo-oh, hold me tight, I'm falling, falling.* . . . It was absurd, but what do you expect ? Even Fate — rather than affront our inconsequence by a sign which would remind us of the age of her family and the respect in which it used to be held — makes herself cheap. The pure profile stammers. By a sort of complicity between her and our way of life she becomes vulgar enough to seem not out of place in the theatre — where our so clever dramatists arrange a few startling, witty, or homely lies in such a way that we pass from our sitting-rooms to the stage — at our wildest, from Hyde Park — without noticing the difference.

*

Only to be a European is to fear. Europe has for long been a continent where the plains are burned dry in summer and frozen in winter by the same fear falling from darkened or clear skies ; where the hills have kept their air of expecting the fugitive ; where rivers are open and navigable to terror from mouth to source. What foreigner, even if he were in Europe and lived through them, can know the weight and shape in our minds of the years during which we watched catastrophe coming towards us behind the idiot mask of Sir John Neville Hoare ?

In the space, cramped enough, of three years, we had five monstrous crises. After March 1938 there was only The Crisis. It was not headlines, or despatches from correspondents. It was fear — it was the taste itself of our bread, it was in the water we drank ; in the air, which for weeks together became dry and heavy, so that the lungs fought with it. In *Siegfried et le Limousin*, in 1922, the most charming of living French writers — and rarely betrayed by his elegance — wrote : *Je ne veux pas mourir avant que les mères dont les fils ont été tués soient toutes mortes : ce jour-là un grand pas sera fait vers le bonheur du monde.* A quite modest wish.

It is the modest wishes of humanity that a war denies. Every glorious (or vain-glorious) wish — for excitement, danger, any severe tension of senses and nerves — are provided for to excess. But the common pleasures, from unbroken hours of reading or conversation with friends, to the coming to our tables of strawberries in their season, are swept away, and with them the common joys — who now rejoices freely in his child's growth to manhood, plans an inheritance, or says : Next year I shall plant a tree here ? Posterity will grieve for its lost treasures, but the real loss is simpler, more tragic, and cannot be put right.

*

IMAGES

They have made an image of you, my dear,
Moulding in your mouth's refusal to smile
A sly wisdom sadder than a tear.
This knowing dead woman is not you. I'll
Help you to undress now, my helpless one,
Night's begun, the long night, nothing can be done

But let you go to sleep. So night may take
From deep of eye-pit some young waking look,
Yes, a girl. What light springs in the opaque
Dark, giving back the living face night took ?
Impatient, you couldn't endure to walk
At your child's pace ; silent. Is it you can't talk ?

O useless. They are all buried, those young
Impatient women, and the bright hair ruined
By neglect, where memory should have clung :
The images hide each other, eyes find
Strange colours in my mind, voice mutes voice, your breath
Clouds only the glass emptied by your death. . . .

Today the rose burns in your face. What cold
Turns thus to grace, teaching you foolish lies ?
Corruption's pupil. Yet what if this new mould
Held ; if freed by their folded lids your eyes

Now smiling secretly beguile your face
To take itself lightly back from your vague race.

You are not in this last image, this mouth
Drowning all past words with its frigid cry,
Coldness unlit by a remembered south.
Have you forgotten how you'd sit and try
New hats, turning from the mirror to ask
Your remote gaze, But does it suit me ?   O quick,
Slipping from me, mute eyes noting my trick,
What young woman looks from me to the glass ?

ELEGY

I

Snow will not fall on her from the hedge
Nor the wind touch her
Nor by stone walls moss-covered her feet carry her
Nor in the streets she knew, loved ;
Resting, now, in a narrower street.
Lane, moors, town, O town,
Give back what you took,
Her pressure, reflection in you.

2

A life squeezed into three words
Into an old woman by the fire chanting
Yes my dear. Yes my dear.
And afterwards, after her death,
Her daughter hears the same voice
Issue from her own body ;
The whole of her childhood, acts, gestures, hands,
Is in that voice freshly flowing through the generations.
Water flows outlasting in a stone runnel
The decayed cloister, under the living frieze of the birds.

3

So if I look into the glass,
Look long and carefully,
Shall I not force her to come forward
Separate herself from its depths
From the reflections waiting, pressed close, in there,
Lean towards me, as when she leaned
And looked into herself minute after
Minute, seeking what knowledge ?

The glass must be keeping her unflawed,
Unused : a king's tomb shelters the seed
Closed in it, life enclosed in that husk,
As all her days, roads she walked on,
Clouds, trees, houses, gathered into her eyes
When she was within touch here
Are laid up, living, uncalled-on, in her image
Withdrawn into the glass : but irreturnable.

4

This is your last night with us.   Forgive me
For anything I when you lived thought against you
In moods viler than the sharp enmity
Of a child.   Forgive me.   And forgive me too
All I selfish did not do for you.   Mind
Me in your smiling death only as the child
I was, stubborn but timid, eager, kind,
When, if I but vexed you lightly, I cried.

*

Paris, rue de l' Abbé de l'Épée.

This room on the top floor of a shabby hotel, this attic, rather,
identified itself instantly with the room I lived in in London
before the last war.   In the moment of waking, and for a moment,
my hand on the coarse sheet gave me back my light awkward
body of those days.   Then, with the grief of re-entering a
stupider body, I had another moment of pleasure to find how
easily it adapted itself to the ways of life of a poor student.
There are certain individual experiences we do not (as, obsessed
with time, Proust thinks) summon to us again and again, so
truly as we live in them perpetually.   They form a space round
us — easily distinguishable among all the other as precisely
formed spaces we are in the habit of walking into.   Whatever
the life we lead here, the shock of recognition itself is pure
happiness.   Why ?   I think, because the mind feels an affection
for what it once, with the greatest care and energy, constructed.
It may when it comes to die feel for the body only affection,
longing, regret.

I re-enter an experience with joy even if in the very moment
I recognise it for one where I am only unhappy :   behind my

anguish, part of it, is the relief with which I stroke a known wall, note the arches I myself built to take the weight of a grief, the windows directing just so much light and, carefully-spaced, the columns leading to the other door.

This attic is narrow, its bed, table, chair, wardrobe, of the cheapest, and defaced by years of rough ill-use. On either side of me, similar attics are lived in by students — last night I heard one of them repeating to himself again and again a series of formulae, and sighing heavily as he knocked each into the walls of his skull. The window looks across the tiles of lower and still shabbier houses to — oh, happiness and glory — the dome of the Panthéon. How many years, far too many, I have waited for Paris, and now I bring it, to live in a student's poor room, the mind and body of a middle-aged writer. Yet I am at home in this room. My mind recognises 'it, stretches itself in it — lighter than it was yesterday, free. The light of a September morning in Paris is not too crushing for it, exacts without cruelty, almost invites.

Yet it was a strict light. It spared nothing. Yard, window-sill, geranium, naked body, its spine a grey cord knotted under the grey skin, standing to wash itself in the window, were outlined by a silence which was really appalling. The noise, of lorries, horns the thumb pressed remorselessly, and voices, rolled over and round them without breaking into the loneliness imposed on each by the light. They were separated, untouchable. Nothing here could comfort itself by gliding into another thing. Each explained itself by the absence of all the rest. It was exhilarating and alarming. I began to understand what a friend had said to me : The first days in Paris you will feel like committing suicide ; after that there's no place like it. I began to see that until the mind has grown a second skin as impenetrable as the light, the assault on it of all these isolated things could be as painful as sand driven into a naked body. It could become intolerable.

Going downstairs, I passed the servant who spends her whole day, from early morning until dark, scrubbing and sweeping. In the cheap hotels of this quarter — I paid one and threepence a day for my room — the dust is ceaselessly polished into floors, furniture, walls. By now, most of them have a second self, indestructible, of dirt.

My landlady, a woman about forty, was in her room on the ground floor, the door open, while her hair was waved. Looking in the glass she could watch it as well as note who came in and out. In a monotonous voice she was telling the hairdresser that her husband had spent the night " with those women ", and was asleep in his room. " First thing when he wakes he'll ask me to give him a clean shirt, and then what money I have in the drawer. What disillusion ! "

The lines of her mouth formed a single word, of surprise and bitterness.

The streets here, behind their mask, unsmiling, of sunlight, are grey and hard with age. The life going on continuously, every inch occupied by it, in every room someone coughing, working, bartering, baking, or pressing offal into a cheap pâté, ironing, giving birth, dying, was self-supported and self-devouring, completely cut off, by a hard membrane, from the soil. There must be living roots, but how far down, and what catastrophe would be strong enough to throw them into the light ? Never, not in any other city, have I felt this division, this separateness, this sense of a brittle ferment, sharply enclosed — in a wide space, true : wide enough to hold, under a delicately-modelled sky, the Sainte-Chapelle, the Seine and its bridges, the Luxembourg, to shelter a great people of monuments, of the past, and a greater weight of treasures of all ages, to hold Notre-Dame, the Place de la Concorde and the Champs-Élysées : but enclosed. The life not only of one city : the Paris of the Middle-Ages, of the seventeenth century, of the Second Empire, of a dozen other distinct epochs, persisted in side-streets, in sunken dilapidated rooms, as well as in the museums where fragments of the past still keep their power to reach out to stroke or twist a nerve. I have been alone in a great many places, but nowhere except here do I feel this irresistible need to be on guard, almost all the time.

*

Not quite. Over breakfast — at the corner of the rue t.-Jacques — I could relax. The sun on the old houses was suave and friendly ; a freshness, almost a salt freshness, sharpened the air : a young lively boy passed, pressing yard-long rolls of bread under an arm, and went with them into the pissoir ; an old woman sauntered, holding a bunch of marigolds between black-gloved hands and smiling. There were a few workmen at the counter, taking their first drink of the day ; they had an air of amiable leisure.

You walked past here, I thought — greatest of mediaeval teachers — exultant, arrogant, until the day when you became he who no longer had the politeness of heart to love anyone, any human being, even the one in whose hands your mind, humiliated with your body, would have been safe. I watched him pass with long strides down the centre of the narrow street ; he avoided the slippery gutter where I fell yesterday, and walked through and obliterated the living bodies of men and women like midges.

My companion stretched her arms. " How well I feel ! "

I watched her with affection and envy. In Paris, as anywhere, she was alive with a strong vigorous ease. Her life was as spontaneous as the unfolding of a strong bud. Nothing hindered in her the fulfilment of a desire except a material circumstance she was too poor, or too unknown, to remove. She was endlessly inquisitive, and with an equal courage. A German, she belonged to that generation, children during the War, whose adolescence was shaken by the collapse of all standards — the mark, the State as Power, the authority of parents, morals. Nothing need be respected. With impotent violence — so much had been destroyed already, so much had failed them, why should it too not be ruined ? — they mocked and tore down the past. The past gone, the future went with it ; they had only a moment in which to enjoy everything they could seize.

At sixteen, she was earning her living in the frenzied Berlin of the early twenties and, with her ruthless self-possession, enjoying it. Her body was her own, to do with as she pleased, strong — a Prussian can feed on hunger — curiously untouched. At twenty-nine she had the face of a girl, and youthfully candid. Prussian as she was, her mind had been bent into rejecting any authority. It is true that the negation of Prussia is anarchy —

what else can it be ? — but she kept firmly all the habits of her childhood, a rigorous neatness, respect for intelligence, and an instinct to possess the world — her first attempt took her to France ; she was almost without money and she managed to live there for several weeks and reach Marseilles. When the Nazis took over Germany she came to England, determined above all not to think or feel as a refugee : the Prussian arrogance under her gaiety and youth refused every weakness as well as every remorse of the exile. She made friends, she worked, she spoke and wrote in English. Poor, she was able to enjoy the life of a young man about town and without sacrificing either her independence or her smiling simplicity, as firm as her will.

We lived in Paris at the rate of her purse : she was not willing to borrow mine. There were so many cheap cafés in this quarter that in some danger of being poisoned we spent, each of us, twelve or fifteen francs on the day's meals. What in my Prussian was the recklessness of youth was in me courage — before the White Russian and Chinese menace.

There is — there was one other person with whom I could have lived easily in such discomfort : for all others I should only feel responsible. She and the young German had the same sensuous quickness and wit, a natural lyricism in act, so unlike my slow ways, and the same purely instinctive charm. Only, since she was a young Englishwoman, she was the subtler, the more intuitive, with a touch of sly malice.

You were my only friend at that time, and perhaps the one always closest to me. Together, we had the stupidity to be young. We shared the squalor of rooms in old houses, of desires, the squalor itself of youth. Ah, Georgina, why need you have died then ? There was still so much you had to do. The curiosity, endless, of your senses, had touched only a few of the things they were offering you. You had changed so little life into yourself. How you would have sat here, indolently smiling, amused by letting the street come to you with its stalls, narrow windows full of figs, cheap hats, pâtés, the church, women haggling, the golden September light. And afterwards you would have walked, drawing glances and aware of them, past windows where without vanity you saw yourself — to find other places where you could give yourself up to seeing. In you, as it is in me, seeing was a passion. It made you selfish and happy. No one, not even this young German, has more than your gift of happiness. You spent it on everything in your life, and on me. I was not thankful enough for it.

No, you were not good. But after the few people who are nerves of my body, in whom runs my blood, I loved you better than the others. That did not make me loyal to you. You had a presentiment when you said smiling,

" That North Sea you are so fond of is treacherous. I don't think I trust it, even in summer."

I have found it easier to be loyal to people I care less for. And then, with age, I am becoming less unstable.

A porter returning from the Halles came into the bistrot. He was sweating and filthy, an animal in the strength and smoothness of his muscles. The look on my young German's face astonished me by its pure response and greed.

" Look at that strong sunburned fellow," she said, seriously : " I admire him, I should like him to be my lover."

" Probably he would beat you."

" I should make him wash and, don't you see ?, teach him to respect me."

" Not in a hundred years," I said, with malice. " Prussian though you are."

She laughed, showing her strong very white teeth. " Yes, you are right. . . . Do you know — I shall never marry. When I am the next year to being forty I shall adopt children, as many as I can get bread for. They will wear my friends' cast-offs, and I shall be kind to them but just — and strict."

*

He was sitting on the narrow pavement of the rue Mouffetard. A wall threw its shadow over him, over his rags, and over his face and its wrinkles — they were like dried-up streams with only a little dirt at the bottom. He was so old that he had outlived the last least flicker of thought in his brain. Or so it seemed until, moving with infinite caution, he pushed very lightly forward one of the broken bits of rubbish, indescribabl old, dirty, worthless, he imagined he was going to sell. Was anyone poor enough, even here, to think of buying one of these filthy pieces of rag, broken handleless cups, a single greasy slipper? " But does he think he is going to sell them? " Did he expect anything now? Yes. For an instant, when a passer-by hesitated, his eye flickered, a spark appeared, then vanished leaving only its absence. It was scarcely to be believed — except that both of us noticed it — that he loved this rubbish. Every few minutes his hand, the only part of him still expectant and alive, stole out to rearrange it. He spent an endless patience and tenderness on placing the stump of a knife so that it caught the light, and his fingers when he shook out a rag in which some threads of colour showed faintly, lingered on it, stroking and smoothing. You could think that these objects still held some mystery for him.

" Why does such a man live? What is being born if for this? *Why* such lives? " Year after year to have arranged his handful of rubbish in infinite space, to have moved his hand in it — for what? To please whom? For whom, at what level of this space, to notice, to be moved? Think of the unfolding of life in his body, of his mind opening slowly under the rain of impressions. Every gesture he made added to the depth of his life, until now, if anyone were capable of exploring it, its recesses would be infinitely deep. He was not conscious of them, except perhaps, in a deaf way, when his hand touched one of the more precious of his revolting bits of rubbish. But how often am I aware of depth in myself, and how often — usually — only able to rage in a flurried waste of strength at the surface?

A child, a little boy — his mother was bargaining at a stall for some green apples — halted in front of him and looked. The old man stared back. A faint smile, only a trembling of the wrinkles nearest his mouth, was his answer to the child's gravity. The miracle was that he had answered. Turning, the child's mother whisked him away. The old man, slowly, gently, drew the handleless cup a little nearer to him. Look : like any other artist, he spends his time realising himself in these objects. You saw that he had filled the cup full of himself.

A day or two later, when I passed, he was there. He had

E

moved closer to the wall and folded his eyes. A middle-aged woman, his daughter perhaps or a granddaughter, was in charge ; she was keeping herself to herself ; she had no impulse to spill her energy into these things or any others. Her poverty was a hard ulcer in her, and it took all her strength.

*

" Dine with us this evening — rue de l'Université. A man is coming you should meet. You can perhaps write about him."

" A friend of yours ? "

" Wait. Wait until you've seen him. . . ."

No, since he grew up, this man had never had a friend. He had colleagues, who were tools, rivals, victims. The little I knew about French politics persuaded me that he would return to office — he had for some time been out. No one could over-bid him in rapacity, guile, corruption. As things grew worse, these powers would call out irresistibly to be used. He had, too, a humour which gave him warmth — and warmth is above all the quality lacking in political life. He ate and drank greedily, and talked with a smiling candour about the vices of his late colleagues.

" They all have a secret they are ashamed of," he said : " or a quite little dream which is a joke or the spit image of a vice." He laughed like a schoolboy. " You think I'm too sly to dream. How wrong you are ! Do you want to see my private joke ? . . . There will be no war in Europe. Why should there ? This country is not fit to oppose Germany, and if the English in the next few years change their minds they'll find they're too late, and they'll be knocked out. What a mercy for the world ! What pickings ! No, no, we shall make a proper and perfectly necessary arrangement with the Germans and behind them advance into the next phase of history — it's because they have forestalled us in it that they are now the strongest. Do you know what I mean ? The epoch of internal ruthlessness. We shall keep our soldiers — there are other continents, and backward compared to Europe — but the power, the real power, will be in the hands of the police. It will be secret and entirely effective. Ears will open everywhere ; in every family on member will be employed by it, unknown to his wife or his son. Should any person, man or woman, old or young, professor, civil servant, workman, begin to talk like a rebel, he will disappear. For the others, the disciplined citizens, we shall do enough to keep them happy. After all, what is happiness ? To eat, to argue over a glass of wine, to sleep with or thrash your wife. No one who behaves himself will go short of these joys. The Germans, by the way, are typically clumsy — with their Dachaus. When my police execute a criminal it will be as secretly as if they were doing it in their sleep — and the consciences of other people will be quiet. I dislike offending consciences. There is nothing I dislike so much, except, possibly, being insulted by chatter about natural laws and the honour, the honour, mark you, of a nation. A nation has honour precisely as it has fleas — on this or that body. The statesman who talks of honour — unless he means something else, quite different — is a rogue. . . . I believe we shall have a little trouble with rogues. But it will pass."

When he had gone my host said,

"He enjoys pretending to be the new Fouché. . . . You're trembling — you mustn't be so simple."

I had grown cold. A joke is a joke or the image of a truth. . . . There have been dictators and ruthless powerful men who have got rid of their enemies : this man, if he has the power, will murder as well the simplest things, the child's trust in his father, the man's in the trivial circumstances, sensuous or gentle, of his life, the woman's in the chairs she polishes and the bread she bakes. His was the pure instinct to be separate, the lack in one thing of all the others, that I had felt here, and he carried it to its ultimate. When he had done his work, there would only be dissolution and distrust. The poison always threatening us, asleep in the veins, in the oldest rocks of our inner world, would move and suddenly get rid of us — this time all. I had come here, to Paris, to learn this.

*

The same friend who believes that part of a writer's experience is to catch his own hidden cruelty reflected in the world took me with him to a house in the avenue Émile-Acollas. In the long anteroom, a double line of footmen like freshly-painted lamp-posts ; at the door of the drawing-room, the last pair, speaking together, repeated the names. The drawing-room was full of people, the women unbelievably elegant, as if each had been drawn for the occasion. The four lustres in the corners of the ceiling drew up brittle rays of light from jewels and finger-nails, crossing and returning them, so that the heads of the guests hung from glittering wires. I was unwilling to move about. Certainly I was out of place here, but it was not likely that any of these people would notice me, except to avoid me as if I were the angle of a chair. I knew that I was alive, but I was not certain any of the others were. This allowed me to feel indifferent.

Our hostess interested herself vaguely in writers. There, against a wall, was the wealthiest of French publishers. And here was that young writer, essayist and poet, who has a singular talent for splitting off layers of personality until these lie round him like finger-nails, on which he draws eyes and a mouth. It is his way of avoiding the remarkable grace and wit so many French writers of this century show in the profound statement of platitudes. There is no doubt that they are, on an average, more intelligent than their English contemporaries, but so much of their brain-work is nothing else. I think, too, that they have begun to live on their capital, on Montaigne and Racine and La Bruyère — Valéry, their last great poet, who spent twenty years in accumulating capital of his own, must be — how old ? — sixty ? And Claudel ?

There was a stir in the anteroom. Looking round I saw the lines of tall footmen bending like poplars, but towards each other. A single guest was announced as His Excellency. . . . I did not hear the rest of it. He was, as soon as he came in, deli-cately mobbed. The young writer was presented to him and rubbed his mind across and across the new-comer's ankles, with feline warmth. Women offered him, spitted on a glance or a tongue, their devotion, as much of it as the wires drawn through their heads allowed them to show.

" Who is it ? " I asked my friend.

" Surely you know the German Ambassador ? What are you thinking ? "

" That it is a rehearsal."

Toute pensée émet un Coup de dés. If, after exposing your mind blankly, like an idiot, to another person or to a scene, you reply instantly to the question : What do you think of . . .?, the image springing from the mirror surface of your mind will resemble a truth. There was the humiliating evening in London when — I was very young and no one in the room knew me, not even my hostess who had smiled gently and absentmindedly when her friend presented me to her. For an hour I sat and watched without thinking. I was leaving, and my hostess spoke to me. " What did you think of S——? If you would like him to read anything you have written, let me see it. He can do a great deal for a young writer."

Alarmed, jerked, by being suddenly spoken to, out of my looking, " He is not interested," I said, " in young women."

She looked at me with such severe rebuke that I thought I should burst into tears. " Don't repeat foolish gossip," she said coldly.

It was only years later I learned that S—— — of whom my ignorance had never heard — was homosexual.

*

There is perhaps a Montmartre which could still be lived in by a foreigner — who was prepared to wrap himself, as refugees do, in his poverty, only taking it off to sleep, or to walk in one of those streets, completely unlit, where the rumour is confirmed that there is a sky and stars, even a moon. One night towards one o'clock I felt my way along a street, after a visit to German artists living — it would be fairer to say that from day to day they existed a little less — in a narrow stone basement near the Place du Tertre. (At this hour the square was empty, except of a few trees which turned out, surprisingly, to be real.) There was a moon, very feeble. I was looking up, and I stumbled over the foot of a heap of rags lying in a doorway. The heap shifted, and an arm, bare to the shoulder, moved like a tentacle under the half-frozen light.

" Even in your bed you're not left in peace."

The woman's sleeping voice, old, hoarse, had kept a tremor of invitation, as though, living in these obscene rags, it now were the prostitute and could only repeat its acts. The arm flung out was held together by strong tendons. Nearly asleep again, she rolled into the light and lay with her rags falling apart on her thigh and a breast. The flesh had perished, and you saw as if laid open the hidden organisation of the body — marvellous even in ruin, a labour of construction which must have demanded infinite skill. You could understand why the voice clung to it.

There is somewhere in the Landes a church which has been worn down by neglect and the salt air ; its walls seem to be ribs and indestructible. A stone figure, all that remains of the tomb of some family, is laid in the porch. The mouth smiles, with a young candour. Immortality even in decay, and a rough patience. The woman, the old worn-out prostitute or beggar . . . was she a woman, is the church a church ? Or are they both a single gesture of the work-worn hand, grasping, still young, of their country ?

*

These tapestries, it says, were woven about 1500. *Les Vendanges.* A much nearer past gathers itself there, among the neat roots of flowers scattered thickly over the ground, and it breaks over me before I can turn aside. Here are all the exquisite glowing colours of the beds of tulips and forget-me-nots in the Valley Gardens in Scarborough. The air is fresh with spring and salt with the sea at the end of the road. The steely North Sea. My mother looked at the beds of tulips as though she were leaning on them, as though they could give her everything she had missed if only, if only, she could look long enough for the colours, the shapes, to plant themselves, leaves, thick green stems, wet earth, all, in her. And with them the noisy rooks and the light. Oh, and the many streets of large and small villas, so ordinary, so nothing, you would think, beside houses she had seen in New Orleans or Cadiz, but she admired them with such eagerness that when with a sigh she gave up trying to own the tulips we turned away at once to walk through street after

street, slowly, that she might absorb the details of their common-
place architecture, and the windows, the many curtains — it
was the era of short curtains stretched on rods across the lower
half of windows, the side curtains not keeping out enough of
the light — all in some way significant for her. Deeply. So
that it never occurred to me even to feel bored by this pilgrimage.

There is a root of daisies in one tapestry. From it, as in one
of those long Chinese paintings, unrolls endlessly a childhood
so far away that I can stand and look at it. However long I
stay looking I shall not see more than a fraction of that infinity
— bounded by the rooms and garden railings of the first house
I remember living in with her. Everything I can see is clear,
but silent, an unbreakable silence. The curtain of coloured beads
on the stairs parts without a sound ; knocked by a finger-nail,
the ostrich-egg rings back silence ; feet press without a creak
up and down, up and down, the wooden stairs ; the taps drip
soundlessly, the laburnum ripples as though in water ; pressing
the earth against the root of crimson daisies she bought in the
market this morning, my mother's fingers, quick, work-swollen,
are more silent in their patience than her eyelids when she looks
up, and frowns, at the child stepping on the freshly-raked border.
How clumsy, how far-off, today how changelessly falsely near.

*

A statue in wood, not more than six or seven inches, of a
pregnant woman : warm-coloured and smooth, the wax rubbed
and worn to a glowing skin : upcast eyes, forehead wrinkled in
distress and gently smiling mouth, young thighs flowing down
from the creased waist. Georgina, if what you bore had not
been death, it could be you — you in your smiling self-absorption,
your almost slatternly playing with life, and careless loss of the
future. It was this loss that pressed lightly against the spine
and it curved inwards, and between the narrow shoulders. The
future tore you out of itself and let you fall and lie where
you fell. There is more of you in this fourteenth-century
wooden carving than in the grave I have not seen. Nor shall
take the trouble to see.

*

Is there any people in the world which has more curiosity, a more purely destructive power of curiosity, than the French? Or is it only the intellectuals, and among them only one generation, which destroys in knowing? Their virtuosity is admirable, and they live, I think, to show it off, to exercise it.

A few tables of the café faced the lively shabby rue Soufflot. With two young to middle-aged writers, Frenchmen born in a province, yet, and easily, natives of Paris, I was waiting to be joined by an English writer, their, not my friend. They began talking about the war which they said must come now — in a year or a few months. One of them took from his pocket the notebook in which he was drafting the scenes of a play about Ulysses. The last but one scene was between Ulysses and Antinous. . . .

Ulysses.—My dear boy, you bore me. And if that were all — at my age one expects young men to be boring. But I know that the violence — natural at your age — of your ideas, still more your admirable speeches, are going to provoke the very disaster you fear. Why not leave well alone?

Antinous.—I don't understand you. You hear the reports travellers are bringing in now every day. You know the strength of the barbarian army. And you shut your ears. If you have a subtle policy, explain it to me.

Ulysses.—It's simple. I prefer peace.

Antinous.—Absence of war isn't peace.

Ulysses.—You have no idea how closely — to a soldier — it resembles it. This morning I woke early. Everything was clear, with the clearness of a pure windless sky. Everything was young. And you can believe me that at my age I know what it is to look at the young world. I saw my wife leaning into her mirror, I saw the light flowing over my fields and along the hill-sides covered with olive-trees — and behind them a bright thread, the sea. My sea. I knew then what you don't — yet. A day on which there is no war is pure gain, worth any cost. You have no wife to look at you in her mirror. No olives ripening.

Antinous.—Would they make me a coward?

Ulysses.—Try your insults, my friend, on a man who hasn't

seen the change in many young men's faces when they died.
You can believe me. The absence of a weight of earth on your
mouth and eyelids, if it is not peace, is a passable likeness. Well
worth having. Friendly.

Antinous.—I see. To enjoy a few years, or only a few months,
of an illusion — you'll sacrifice a generation.

Ulysses.—I felt sure we should have that ! You think, perhaps, that yours is a unique generation ? It would be a scandal
to lay hands on you ?

Antinous.—And you lie. You tell people there's nothing
to be alarmed at, they can go on horse-racing and arguing, no
need for them to store weapons, oil, corn. In a less honourable
man, it might be cowardice. I think that in you it's a mortal
laziness and the fear of change. Ulysses the far-sighted. Perhaps
you find these epithets in poor taste now. . . .

Ulysses.—What do you want me to do ? I've lived, remember, through one war. And through the twenty years since it
ended in a victory. We'll go on talking of it as a victory. . . .
They haven't been easy.

Antinous.—Yes, yes, I know all about the causes you weren't
able to control. Do you still prefer to call them gods ? They
wrecked your plans. Had you one, except to get home to
Penelope and your bed ? And they started disasters from which
somehow you always escaped. Others of your friends were
less lucky. Yours has been a hard fate, Ulysses. All during the
war you were a leader, not one of the first, but in a responsible
position. You were respected ; you made a name for yourself
as a clever patient statesman. The mental habits you share
with the more cunning animals became, before the war ended,
marks of prudence and common sense. Even in the last difficult
years you enjoyed some delightful intervals. . . . You have
earned your Penelope and you want to enjoy her. How natural !
And us ?

Ulysses.—I am an elderly man, Antinous. The future is in
your hands. You will live it, you are responsible for it.

Antinous.—Good. You are going to abdicate. . . .

Ulysses.—My dear Antinous !

Antinous.—The future is ours. The responsibility is ours.

And the power, all the power, yours. Hypocrite !

Ulysses.—Tell me — suppose I retire in your favour — what would you do ?

Antinous.—Warn the barbarians. And re-arm our people. Quickly !

Ulysses.—Too late. Their army is ready and your warning would begin the invasion. Do you imagine they would give you time after it to re-arm ? Out of politeness ? . . . My dear boy, I implore you to go on writing poetry. It limits the amount of harm you can do and leaves me in peace to find the safe way out of our danger. I'm used to it. I've done it for twenty years. And, if I may say so, I've done it well.

Antinous.—Ah, you admit they mean war !

Ulysses.—I admit nothing. Least of all, that the way to prevent war is to begin one. . . . When you go out this evening, look round you. Look at the hands of the men who have been sweating in the olive-fields all day and are seated, arguing or drowsily silent, over their glasses of dark wine. Listen to the women talking as they chop herbs to put in the soup. Watch one of them take her child up to carry him indoors, and imagine what you won't forget when you have seen it — I have — the moment when he is taken from her and killed, there, under her eyes. All this peaceful life, these early mornings of waking in the clear light to another long day of work flavoured with garlic and rough wine, these long evenings of half-drunken talk, the nights lying beside a familiar but still pleasurable and useful body — days and nights which are nothing in the eyes of a clever young man, and in the life of a nation, everything it has . . . you want to wipe it out at once — because it may, perhaps, be attacked next year or in two years. Poet !

Antinous.—Actor ! Your love of Ithaca is one of your most moving traits. How touching ! And how useful it has been to you.

Ulysses.—Antinous — you make the usual mistake of a clever man. You imagine that because you see through me you see me.

Antinous.—I see a subtle politician, swollen with honours, and afraid of losing his lands and his wife.

Ulysses.—You know Penelope's opinion of you.

Antinous.—And Penelope, too, is middle-aged.

Ulysses.—How fit you are to govern !

Antinous.—Go on governing us, Ulysses. We are not rebels. We only ask to be governed. And told the truth. And armed.

Ulysses.—In the middle of the olive harvest ? Impossible. For the next few months I need every skilled man I have. You want to turn my pruners and goatherds into soldiers, and at the same time you want peace ! No doubt I'm senile, but I have my ideas.

Antinous.—We ask nothing better than to understand and obey you, Ulysses. Go on.

Ulysses.—Has it never struck you that with a little encouragement the barbarians may turn on some weaker country ?

Antinous.—And afterwards ? When they are excited by easy victory ?

Ulysses.—Or sated. . . . We can, I think, leave the future to the gods.

Antinous.—Is that your plan ? After all your promises and admonitions you can only offer an excuse for doing nothing ? For falling asleep after dinner and waking to bore us all with another version of your travels. Poor Penelope ! . . . Very well. You refuse to warn our people. I shall. And at once.

Ulysses.—Antinous, I ask you not to begin brawling now. Between ourselves, I'm at the most delicate stage of my negotiations with the barbarian leader. Everything depends on it.

Antinous.—Another excuse !

Ulysses.—I forbid you.

Antinous turns away. During the whole scene Ulysses has been handling and adjusting his bow : he lifts it quickly, and the arrow pierces Antinous in the side.

Antinous.—Old — coward — and disgraced. . . . The future . . .   *He dies.*

Ulysses.—My poor boy. And what nonsense. The future is always on the side of the records. And you and your friends will not have written them. Admit, too, that I tried to spare you. I'm nothing if not patient. And reasonable. . . . These young men are very unlucky. There are men who are born

unlucky — he was one of them — and it was not that I disliked him. In fact I liked him. . . .

*

The first important scene of the play — between Penelope
and Ulysses — was unfinished. It took place the day after his
return. Penelope, her author said, was modelled on the prefect's
wife of a department, south of the Loire, not rich, not much
visited, none of its vineyards known outside the commune which
cherished it, a modest handsome county, with its due share of
scandals, envy, young marriageable girls, cousins, and easy happiness. The prefect's wife had smooth heavy arms, which could
still make the gestures of her angular girlhood, just as her mind,
in some disregarded corner, kept the vivacity and warm-hearted
malice of the young girl. . . .

Ulysses.—Penelope !

Penelope.—My love ?

Ulysses.—Ah, it's really you. For a moment I didn't know
where I was. Is this our room ? Is that really your great-
grandmother's mirror ?

Penelope.—Yes — I'm sorry to say it is. And just as cloudy
and unsatisfactory as ever. You really must ask the captain
of one of your ships to bring me a new one from Massalia. I
hoped — but, there, my dear Ulysses, I suppose you had more
important things to remember. And when you left, it was less
necessary than it is now that I should see myself clearly.

Ulysses.—You have changed during these years. You are
another and lovelier Penelope. . . .

Penelope.—Thanks from all the others — the Penelopes you
missed.

Ulysses.—Were there many of them ?

Penelope.—Several. There was the one whose waist you
were able to span between your hands — she was rather a little
idiot. A second, though she could still outrun her women — but
perhaps they cheated — was occasionally a little, oh a very little
tired after a long day when the bailiff and her dressmaker had
been tiresome. Another discovered quite suddenly that it's not
in the least amusing to walk barefoot in the wet grass. And

yet another — but you don't want to meet all these strangers.

Ulysses.—I have my faithful, my adorable wife——

Penelope.—Middle-aged, a good housewife, and easily made happy — by things her younger self took without noticing . . . a perfectly ripened fig, the new wine, and, how rare and marvellous, one of those hours when everything, from the air to one's less young body, feels new and light.

Ulysses.—Do you find me very old ?

Penelope.—You are all I remembered you as being.

Ulysses.—Dear Penelope !

Penelope.—And now, my love, I must talk to you a little about Telemachus. . . . How thankful I am that we had only one child, and there will be no trouble about the estate. . . . He is a dear boy, more like your family than mine, but he hasn't, alas, your placidity. Perhaps I spoiled him just a little. . . . I think marriage — not that I intend to lose him. . . .

Ulysses.—We can discuss it. But I haven't told you anything about my voyage——

Penelope.—Another time — this evening — or during the winter, if you can keep awake after dinner. I'm longing to hear it. But now I simply must go and talk to them in the dairy. You've no idea how lazy and flighty girls are now — and with these boys about, and the men coming back — I expect the worst.

Ulysses.—I'm afraid you're not interested.

Penelope.—My dear !

Ulysses.—And there are some things I ought to explain. . . .

Penelope.—No. Certainly not.

Ulysses.—But why not ? Surely you don't think that anything I have to tell you will offend your ears, your — small — neatly-curled — ears. Let me touch one of them.

Penelope.—You would be careful not to tell anything that could offend me.

Ulysses.—I don't understand you.

Penelope.—My love, I have the most complete trust in your discretion and knowledge of human nature. Of my nature at least. Like any sensible woman of my age I would rather you deceived me than made me cry. Tears would be fatal to my skin. The maids are already telling each other stories they have picked up from the sailors — I am sure that if I could hear it the whole quarter down by the harbour is as full of murmurs as those shells children hold against their ears — stories about young women they call sirens. Now, now, my dear Ulysses, I'm not a girl, and you needn't explain that a siren is a sort of tropical fish. Nor do I want you to tell me anything about Calypso except whether she still plucks her eyebrows and makes all her guests uncomfortable by begging them not to leave on the day arranged . . . dear Calypso — even as a girl she was tiresomely intense, and I always knew she would be unhappy. If Madame Circe gave you the recipes of any of her dishes I should be glad of them. She must have a marvellous cook. And Nausicaa, the dear child — you shall tell me how tongue-tied she was and whether she is worth considering for Telemachus. But that's all. If you're tactless enough to try to tell me anything I don't wish to hear, I shall close my ears. Like this. My love, you understand me perfectly. When I was a young woman, I adored excitement and turning my life upside-down. Now all I ask is peace. I want to grow tranquilly old, with my dear tables and curtains and fig-trees round me. I do want a mirror, but if it means any trouble I'll put up with the old one. Dear Ulysses. . . .

*

At no moment in their discussion — it went on a long time — did the danger which plainly threatened France move their minds except as a ball thrown and rebounding from one to the other. They played with extreme brilliance. None of their English contemporaries is capable of such grace and wit. Nor were they showing-off before the foreigner. When timidly I asked what they were going to do, to rouse their countrymen, they made my question the spring-board for another flight of analytical wit. Clearly, except in this way, they could not take it seriously. Their duty to France was finished when the figure of Antinous had been invented to carry their fear, contempt, insight — and to die of the prudent greed of his elders. No doubt it was a form of protest. It seemed to me equally a desertion. I was afraid to say this.

We were joined by their English friend, an adolescent of forty, lazy, narrowly cultivated, an admirable essayist by his skill in weaving ideas, not complex, not his own, into a neat border. It must have been he who began talking of our debt to France. To neither Frenchman would it have occurred to say in so many words that, apart from Shakespeare, we had nothing, no one, to set with the glorious crowd of French writers from Ronsard to Éluard. Certainly they believed it — half deliberately, and half by a firm instinct. French writers are drawn, a gleaming thread, through the life of mediaeval and modern Europe. And certainly in the nineteenth century they ran, athletes and nervous, outstripping our complacence and vested beliefs. But — all our Elizabethans, all the complex harmony of our seventeenth century, all our superb Augustans ? A coward as usual, I sat and morosely said nothing, but thought, about my countryman : You snob. Only a strange snobbery could bring an intelligent man to abolish, so lightly, his inheritance.

His French listeners were amused, and I was aware of their not quite hidden contempt. They were far from denying anything he said, and they were surprised he said it. It confirmed, I think, their belief, ironical and instinctive, in the mental poverty of all countries except their own.

" There are," I said at last, " English writers, even alive, who are worth reading, and in their own language."

" I am sure of it," the younger Frenchman said gravely. " It remains true that both of you have read Gide, Mauriac, Valéry, Claudel, Giraudoux, and learned French simply in order to read them, and I suppose Mallarmé, Baudelaire — I won't list the others. Where neither of us reads English. Nor — which is really significant — feels he need. You must need us. Your own literature leaves you hungry — or why come to ours ? "

" We have more curiosity."

He smiled without kindness. He knew they had a greater share of curiosity and intellectual courage than any other people. What he didn't — still doesn't — recall is the fate of Narcissus. Almost every Frenchman is absorbed in the image of his wit, elegance, the superb dance of his faculties. He looks at it, as pleasure, as a duty, and finds there depth on perfect depth of charm and meaning. And while he draws these back into himself, and sees nothing except the one exquisite face, other peoples are forging from themselves new — perhaps grosser, perhaps only other — images, of which he knows nothing. His ignorance is a danger — not only but first to him. Unmolested, he will in time die into his image. No doubt a charming death, and nothing forbids us to believe in his future life. But the gross stammering of other words can break into his perfect syllables and obliterate them.

Or so I feared — and listened. I had no spirit to argue.

I sat drinking my coffee — quite abominable, as French coffee is — trying to understand my own need of the literature of this insular insolent people. And my love, a passion more than of the intellect, of France. I couldn't allow that I, too, am a snob ! Nor, I thought, looking at my wordy countryman again, are you, except when you chase away all our great shades to make a space round the French. What is it I respect ?

Two virtues, above all, of the French spirit. A suavity which seems to belong to the skeleton itself, as though it would be easy in that country of the Marne where they lie together to separate a French from the English bones touching it. An inborn sense of the *possible* — forming out of wine, bread, and leisure, a living classicism, a mode of life which comes nearly to employ without straining them all the human qualities. That the suavity exists in the same mind with an intolerant vanity and rudeness ; that the spiritual tact can become sterile or break down into lawlessness — alters nothing. A world in which, to defend herself, France became less human, would be very disappointing.

It is perhaps enough if she were to become a shade less insular.

*

The Exhibition was still on. We went several times, and tired ourselves in that hot sun, walking from pavilion to pavilion, looking. The great nations, self-conscious and cruelly spoiled by it, tried to make an impression. The Germans and Russians noisily of power ; the English of middle-class comfort ; the

Americans of a massive technical efficiency — dull, if you believed it. Only the smaller peoples had natural good manners and came forward politely and eagerly with their treasures. Some of these were exquisite. There was the clearly straight furniture, recalling forests of birch, strawberries growing wild by the side of steep paths, and the long cool northern summer nights, sleepless. There were glasses which did not need wine to be full of light. And, worth going back to again and again, the fountain of rose-water in the pavilion, small, unpretentious, of Bulgaria. This fountain, simple, almost plain in its scented elegance, asked to be liked. To be grateful was easy. Beside it, everything else was unreal and forced. So much in the Exhibition, if one had not forgotten it quickly, would have been an intolerable weight of ugliness and boredom.

The whole place was a nursery, full of toys. Some of the toys were alarming, some only pitiful or amusing, and others, a very few, were made to be drawn gently into the mind and stored there against the day when the hand groping among the rubble touches a headless doll or a cup, miraculously whole, filled with dust.

*

Paris is a province ; it has its towns, its villages huddled below a vast church, its wide river valley, its palaces and strong old trees. There is the Paris of the Tuileries, of the Sorbonne, of the hospitals and the great boulevards, and the so different Paris of the poor, poorer here than in any other European city ; in the other cities the poorest people turn into animals, where here vestiges of humanity cling to them ; they become a sort of human spittle at the foot of walls and under arches and in foetid basements. But one Paris is unlike all the others, and pitiful ; the Paris of the refugees.

It has no separate existence in space. It exists in time-waves — the wave flung across Europe by the revolution in Russia, later waves starting one behind the other in Germany, in Spain, in Austria. It meets you in any poor or half-demolished street, or on the stairs of hotels shabbier than the one we lived in.

One German I knew was a painter. He need not, since he was not a Jew and his work was unobtrusive and gentle, in

no sense advanced, have left Munich. He left, in 1933, in order
to breathe. What he left was not terror, not disgrace, but an
easy secluded life — his paintings were much admired by all
except the eccentrics whose disgrace he chose to share — for the
extreme harshness of his years in Paris. He was an old man.
You had only to look at him to see that he was good and innocent. Smiles setting out from the corners of his eyes contradicted
the web of grief covering his face. In his room — it was really
a cupboard, half below the stairs of a house sinking under the
weight of its own filth and age — he had a couch, a backless
chair, and a stove where he boiled potatoes. He lived on them ;
they were clean and cheap. He had a friend, much younger, a
Berlin Jew, sickly and gross-lipped. They lived at opposite ends
of Paris and took it in turn to visit each other, of course on foot.

The younger man had a room, a large room, on the ground
floor of a house which had been condemned and was evading
sentence by falling quietly to pieces : you reached it across the
pitfalls of a small courtyard ; a barren vine covered one wall
with its stems and overgrown hairy leaves. He was a writer :
now and then, with a good deal of waiting about and cringing,
he sold an article and had money to spend.

Today he invited me to supper. It was a party, for the
German family, father, mother, and two children, he had taken
under his wing. His wing ! I arrived a little early, and found
him with his friend busy wrapping up a large watercolour that
the old painter — it was a miracle — had sold. To a former
patron who had discovered him in Paris. It was to be packed
and left the next morning at an hotel. Mistrusting his skill, the
painter had carried it across Paris, and now, as gently as though
it were alive, his friend was swaddling it in a piece of checked
cotton, the rags of a shirt, and sheets of paper he had begged
from a shop. His fingers shook lightly with anxiety and love.
He drew me aside to tell me how much the painter had been paid.
It was not much.

We were overheard. " Emil," the painter said reproachfully,
" you are still grumbling. And on a day when I am divinely
happy."

" He could have given you the proper sum."

" But he came to see me in my room," the painter said, smiling, " and he saw how little I spend."

The guests came. Emil made the coffee and put on the table a pound of biscuits and a small bottle of rum. He was pleased and very proud of this feast. Suddenly he saw the painter look in a small bowl on the table and move it stealthily aside. Reaching for it — yes, he had forgotten to buy sugar. At once all his pride was wiped out by shame. He almost wept.

" But, Emil," his friend cried, " the rum ! We'll pour the rum into our coffee. Who wants sugar when he can have strong sweet rum ? "

The children, too, had a few drops of the precious stuff measured into their cups. Their hands, the paws of small animals, stretched out quickly again and again to the plate of biscuits. They ate in silence, accepting the bliss of this moment as gently as they had accepted terror, flight, hunger. Their world — I felt it beginning to open round me — was not, as their parents' was, shut in by hills, with clearly-marked roads leading just so far : to the Prefecture, the bakery, the room where a coat or a little money would, at the price of answering a great many questions, be handed out — not grudgingly and yet as if grudged. The cracked plate with its biscuits rested just within reach, at the edge of all they did not try to understand. Anxiety was reflected on to them, but for hours, for an endless time, they ignored it.

At this moment the others were talking about *papers*. To possess as many francs as would buy a certain paper made the difference between living, however wretchedly, as human beings or as vermin, and hunted. Each time the old painter began to speak Emil interrupted. He was terribly afraid that his friend meant to offer up the sum paid for the picture. In the end, in his sharp Berlin voice, he began singing. He sang *Ich grolle nicht*, and the others, not the children, sang with him.

I could not follow the words. But I caught, rising in the darkness of the room lit by a candle, and from a depth I have not yet touched nor can touch, the strong note of existence itself. To hear it without the long failure of living, would not that be what these children still had, and what I remember I had, a freedom in which the body is so immaterial that it would be no shock if suddenly it became the body of a bird or a tree ?

*

My friend left weeks ago. It is easier to stay in this hotel than to look for another. Besides, I have not much money. And this room suits me. I sit writing, I eat in slightly better cafés, where I am not so likely to be poisoned, and I can come and go on these stairs without meeting a soul. This morning I went into the Luxembourg Gardens and sat there, under the smooth light flowing, a bland oil, round trees, children, stone vase. Pressed into myself by the separateness of everything here, I felt at first only the absence of feeling. It is like that with me so often. Things try — the light striking the dome of the Panthéon, a hand, almost an offering, laid on a café table — to break through the silence to me, but more and more I see only myself, moving among isolated objects which little by little are losing their weight and hardness, their substance, and moving farther off. If I could stay here alone until I began to hear. I know that as soon as I leave I shall lose this . . . attentiveness. I am weakly restless — patience has to be forced on me, by living alone in a place I don't know. The darkness closing round me, the weight on my eyelids, absence or disregard of all other sounds, lead where ? I can imagine at the other edge of this forest light springing, and warmth, smooth and heavy, on my eyes, but I have not the courage to go on, to find my way back, or forward — at this point they would be the same — to a life, a milk pressed for me by a work-worn serene finger, to the sharply-pointed northern air on the fields, to lights sunk — are they of windows or ideas ? — in the so gentle and tranquil night, to the Church, landmark for sailors and pilgrims, on the edge of the cliff, to the voices, stronger than the defaced lettering on its stones, of the long grass, rank and wind-beaten, to a future of riddles, to disinterest. It is easier to turn aside.

I see myself stand up and go away, a stranger and clumsy, along these paths between the reluctant trees of October. I see — but I am deaf.

*

It had rained, and I walked through a great many narrow ill-lit streets, crossed the Seine, and at last, shivering, because the air was cold and still damp, I sat outside a small restaurant and asked for coffee. The dark bulk of the Louvre was near, and there was a street-lamp, a weak cloudy vapour round a stem. Leaning against it a girl and a young man. The light fell on her thin arms straining at his shoulders, and her face, plain, with closed eyes. Desire separated them from everything. They were a single ungentle pain. A cold sleet began falling. She spread her hands above his head pressed at her throat.

*

Last night dreaming my mother alive, and living, by herself, in the end house of that street of houses with narrow sedate gardens which faces the inner harbour, I felt that she was in danger. Heavy with anxiety I went to see her. Three of us drove to the house ; I saw with fear that all the blinds were down. I ran in. The door was open, the floor broken in places, and the walls cracked. I called. To my joy, she answered. She was there, safe ; she must, I said, come and live with me, and we put her in the car and drove off. There was scarcely room for me ; I had to sit on an edge of the seat as — but I did not think of it until I woke — in the car leaving her funeral.

For a long time, in the greyness of this Parisian room, I wondered whether she would forgive me for leaving her.

SECOND BOOK

1938

22 May. I have been with my youngest sister, talking of where we could take her children if war comes in the next weeks : the boy two years old and the child who will be born in a few days or hours.

It seems the last moment of decision. As though the circles are narrowing now quickly and the centre is very close. There is only news of tension — the stretched nerves of a hand waiting to be severed — and of German and Czech troops moving to the frontier between their countries. While I was with her I rang up a friend in London who will always know what is happening in Europe, and repeated what he said — The feeling is that it is not war. My sister, who for a moment had come back nearer to the surface of her life from its inner engrossing task, smiled and went back there, leaving the smile to lie vaguely on the surface, forgotten : she was, as always, too busy.

Before I sleep I must think about her. Think. . . . That old tyrant, my grandmother Mary Hervey, had the same clear coldly blue eyes as my mother — in a vague fear at seeing them go away I laid my hand over them when she died. In my family one man or woman in every generation has these eyes, without a shadow on their blueness : the eyes of all the others are ambiguous, clouded by secrecy and a twisted diffidence ; we are perhaps intimidated and driven into ourselves by the directness, the quick radiance and anger, of this one's look.

Its clearness has been given, in my generation, to my youngest sister. And with it the intense loyalties and hatreds, and the swift frankness, of those of us whom no one, no master for the time of the family, has been able to subdue. She defeated my mother easily. In the early struggle of their wills, hers conquered by its mute rage — of a child of four. True, my mother was tired from her life, but I doubt how much that accounts for her new gentleness and timidity before her last-born. I doubt it because I, too, am careful with her and, yes, timid. I, too —

when I know that she wants something very much — am anxious to give it to her. This has little to do with my will ; it is an instinct ; it springs from a source deep enough to have no name — or I have never taken the trouble to name it. Love ? Responsibility ? Her being young ? . . . It has always been there. . . . I suspect that my mother, too, felt this secret compulsion, blind, but too clear to be disregarded. Half with guilt, she gave all she had. Once or twice she made excuses to me for giving the youngest so much. I encouraged her to do it — but that was because I saw it pleased her and gave her her only deep happiness of this time.

My sister grew up less and less like me — quick-witted, practical, loyal where she loved and pitiless in her dislikes. My energy is patient, hers a quiver starting in the nerves and plunging through her like light through trees. Fair-haired, the natural scarlet, clear, fine, of her lips a sign of her blood's quickness, slender. Deceptively hard — with a kernel of purest unchanging devotion to a few persons — her husband first, her children, me if I am attacked.

She is generous and unforgiving. When she was very young she befriended a stray cat and saved for it every day part of her cup of milk. One day it stole from the pantry. Turning on it with hate, she drove it away and never again allowed it into the house, because it had disgraced itself and failed her.

23 May. I have a niece. In the single glimpse I caught of them I thought her eyes were a light clear blue.

A great many bombing planes in formation passed over the house in the morning. My sister said to herself that war must be coming at once and the Government was trying to reassure us. She waited, to ask about it, until I came, knowing that the nurses would lie, and resenting gentleness as a humiliation, Why did she think I should tell her, at this moment, a disturbing truth ? And she is deeply uninterested, still busy bringing order into this new workroom of her life.

Who will describe for us as they are these days of waiting ? We carry with us everywhere, the whole time, sleeping and awake, the thought and expectation of war. It has already gone on too long. For too long we have been reading about events — and from here some of them look unimportant : a brawl in the streets of a frontier town and a man, a single faceless man, shot ; a meeting of students and flags ; the speech, senseless and noisy, of some local dictator — and wondering whether this nothing meant that it had begun ? Begun ? Has it, for years, even hesitated — that slow movement of a finger towards the lever ? Whole peoples are waiting, men in front of machines or in fields, women quiet after childbirth, and others to whom suddenly the bones of a child's head, or a man's, seem too frail.

Is there any way in which my sister and her family could go away in time ? Perhaps to Canada ? Of course not. With the others, they are caught.

28 August. Part of my mind refuses to attend to this new crisis. It goes on, with intense care, as though everything else were asleep, writing *The Children Must Fear*, for a book in which it will be the last section : written, because it presses in my mind like an anxiety, first. Selfish or insensible ?

You slept, do you remember ?, during her last night.

I can count on the fingers of a hand the persons who would always, in any crisis of their lives, engage my whole attention, with or against my will and without the smallest grain of reserve. My son, my husband, my sister, her two children. . . . It seems that England is not one of these persons, since I can sit here and write instead of listening. The obsession is not far off, and the almost stupid despair. They seize me as soon as I have written all at one time I can, and force me to attend. Until then — I write. I should be ashamed of this unwillingness. Yet what, now, can I do ? What was for years at the other side of the door is in the room. I see it when I look up. If it is going to live here, one might as well get used to it and keep quiet.

Who said that ? Not I. A great many men and women all speaking at once in my blood, in that old blood which I feel sometimes has become too impatient and bored to hold out any longer. There are so few of us now ; at home my father is alone in his house, with the loot of his voyages and the photographs he pastes in books : none of us is willing to live there. He is shabby and grows shabbier. What does he think about in the silence : what comes from a past endured and nowhere shared ?

*

The door opened then. It was my son who, not having said he would come, came in, from his aerodrome. The terror I have been avoiding sprang on me. I can drive it into its cage. I can talk, smile, tell stories, I am quiet. This old trick of women is not wisdom. Cowardice, more like. We agree to too much for our children. The question is not put to us in words we can understand. Do you, they say, want your child to feel that so far as he is concerned freedom, justice, and those other enduring forms into which humanity still keeps trying to pour itself, are less important than he is ? Do you want him to be afraid of pain ? They never say : Are you willing that he should be torn living in pieces ? Can you bear the cold of the earth on his eyes and hands ? Put to us like that, what should we say ? Even those who believe, yes, believe, in life everlasting ? That is, in life. We still want for them this life, down to its smallest bud, this sun, and the least of these stars.

*

I must — before the war comes — clear my mind of the quarrel which has been going on in it for years. Since the time when to my loathing of war was joined loathing of the newest tyranny, an old one adapted and brought up to date by cruelly simple-minded men — first in Russia, where, in spite of the deaths, it seemed possible there were seeds the future was going to spring from (even if, as it grew, it took on more and more the strong Tartar look in its stem and leaves) ; then in Germany. And in Germany, it was too clear, the future was being shut up and tortured in places where all the sickening cruelties of the past had revived suddenly, like seeds left in a tomb. So long as there was a chance, the least, that the war we *knew* was coming would not come, would content itself with carrying off lambs and children from outlying farms, the brawl could go on. I could carry in my mind two refusals, cancelling each other.

I am confused by an agony of fear. That there are millions

of us who have reached the same place is no good. Think, you must think.

Is it true that, except by the unhearing, unseeing, the falsely romantic, the morally or sensually perverted, or the interested, wars are recognised to be cruel, wasteful, deeply useless ?

Is it true that the commonly sensible and intelligent man does not want to become part of a machine for slaughtering men ? But obeys, and for months he prepares himself, with the sacrifice of his time and will, to perform the act which he knows to be inexcusable, and does not excuse — or excuses with hysteria (Montherlant) : or he avoids it in thought. Or — there is the clever young historian who has decided, on the ground that if such crimes must be committed he cannot leave them to others, to train as a bombing pilot — he chooses deliberately to take the worst on himself.

Is it true that the soldier by profession is often less indulgent to war than the non-combatant civilian ? And yet, without remorse, he makes himself responsible for as many deaths as a plague. Sometimes, against the advice of men who know better, he insists on a Passchendaele of young men. What insulating dullness allows him to accept honours, or show himself to the people as if he were an actor and harmless ?

Is it true that we read placidly the phrase : Our losses were *only* . . . ? That we shall check the feeling of pity which will rise in us when, from our own experience, we see and hear what is going on in an enemy town during an air-raid ? As if, at the other side of a frontier, anguish weighed less : as if over there children are not children.

Is it true that war is the opportunity of bullies ? of jacks-in-office ? of men whose greeds are so swollen that in all sincerity they identify them with the nation ?

It is all true.

And true that in certain sensitive people — perhaps in many ? — war calls out their purest good. They dig down in themselves to a gentleness, a selfless serenity, a refusal of ambition, that in the rest of their life nothing reaches. In spite even of boredom, they are content, and it can happen that they feel the loss of this unseen contentment more than they welcome peace.

Have we a right to suppose that this pure passion benefits the race ? None. It exhausts. In the circuit of a few years it discharges the virtue of a lifetime.

The worshippers of the machine do not deny that it lets the Ape in us twist the still living nerve of our humanity with more skill than an executioner of the past winding his entrails from a living man. (A letter from an English airman in Spain : *You needn't be sad if — it should be when ; these are truly awful machines — I don't get back this time. We bombed* (name deleted) *yesterday, I came home tired out and fell asleep almost at once — and had a confused dream about the children I must have killed or only mutilated. All I could say to myself was : Thank God I'm dreaming. But I woke up and it was true.*)

And after wars of the modern sort, we are too bitter and bewildered to make peace. As in 1919, what we shall make is another war.

I meet people who say they are in despair : man is so cruel and stupid that the sooner he, like other unwanted species, dies out, the better. If only I could repeat this, war, and Dachau, would be moments on the way to extinction, and mean nothing. They would be endurable — not simply as anything is that fails to kill — but as a test, an examination, which need not be passed. I can't. Men suffer. When it comes to dying, there are no cruel or stupid men, or enemies. The kernel that death pulls out with his fingers is always the same. He must find it odd to split open so many different-looking fruits and find an identical pulp. . . .

I have not chosen between my pacifism and my dislike of a tyrant — which is older in me than many a fear. Pacifism is easy when you keep your gaze steadily on war, on the Ape's work. Too easy : pacifists are ashamed of this ease, and make the most of their other difficulties. Shift your gaze a little to one side, to Dachau and the schools where children's tender skulls are hardened to deny gentleness and freedom, place them in the England you know — and it is no longer easy, or even possible, to remain a pacifist. This is really the moment of decision. It is no use saying that what one obscure person chooses is not important. That is only another and feeble escape.

Is there a way to hold these evils in the mind, and accepting the guilt of both live quietly in the mortal silence below them — and free of an agony pressing always on the same nerve ? A place in which the twin streams of cruelty and gentleness are joined in a salt freshness the old can look at and the young learn by heart ? There must be. But I know already that my lack of patience will not take me so deep — and when the moment to choose comes, between submission to the evil of war and the evil of Dachau, I shall chose, blindly, the first.

*

In its middle years, my body remembers that girl with her baby, in the room with the high chair set in the window. Who is listening more closely, she or I ? There seems no difference between us, and between the child and the young man scarcely a likeness.

During the last weeks, he said, he had thrown overboard as many as he could lay hands on of all the theories, ideas, and even the emotions, he had learned. Now he wanted to study every branch of knowledge and at the age of fifty write a small pamphlet. Wasn't it, I asked, exhilarating to have thrown everything overboard and have nothing ? Yes, at first, but now he felt dejected and almost sullen. (His happiness broke from him in smiles and slight movements of his long narrow hands. I had thought they would grow up the hands of a surgeon or a writer : as it has turned out they are, and by his early choice, an airman's.)

I spoke of the imperative of our age : to fend off the too many unreal wants thrusting themselves at us. Trying to attend to them cheats us of our seven feet of time ; only by leading very simple lives can we save ourselves. And from the greedy habits of our family. " I'm not greedy," he said : " you gave me a great deal : the Alps, Cambridge, flying. Now all I want is books, companionship, children, and to go on flying." With a smile, he added, " My mind is really so like yours that often I know your thoughts."

At the moment I had a single thought — certainly unseen — shadow, stone dropping in the bitter silence of water : Pray

God take away the war from us. . . . What nonsense that the world is smaller than it was in the time of oil-lamps and sailing ships ! Can I hear what is being said by women in Spain and China ? Not a word.

*

There is in me a landscape of desert and rocky hills : sometimes it sprouts the infant streets of my own memory ; oftener it is placed in a memory so old and savage that it can talk only in signs. This time I was alone in a dazed sandy country, and saw the huge curved uprush through the sky of two birds, darkly crested and strong : others coming behind were crestless. They doubled the flight of the sky. I felt an astonished delight in so much beauty, then anxiety if they should attack us. Us ? There was a formless people on the ground, confused with the stones and the skeleton-like roots of trees. . . . After I woke from this dream, my pleasure in these great birds kept me awake — and the fear they had roused.

*

22 September. This reached me from Prague today :

To the Conscience of the World

In this fateful moment, when a decision between war and peace is being reached, we, the undersigned Czechoslovak writers, address this solemn appeal to all those who form the conscience of the world . . . and so on. It is not a long document, nor is it an appeal. It is more the voice, quietly serious, of a people in the greatest danger, which without violence says : Judge us whether we have deserved to be killed by a stronger and greedier, we who, though in different words, speak your own language of freedom and conscience. . . . *We appeal to all writers and to all others who create culture. . . .*

Who told you, Czechs, that anyone if you called would hear you ? Except those who are already sick with shame. We might have warned you that our advice and admonitions were only delaying the moment when we should leave you with your murderer. That would have been honest. But it would not have been according to the forms. It is always to the forms that a policy of hesitations and confusion attaches itself. I am sure our old men are confused. It must have occurred to them at last that they are dealing with bandits, and the only thing they can think of doing is to ask for a receipt made out in legal form for the goods handed over. These include the children I saw, three months since, march with their springing step through Prague for the great meeting of the Sokols. Small groups had trained over the whole country, keeping time to the same music : when they came together for the first time, in the stadium, they moved as a single supple body, with the lightness of a dancer.

How young Prague was this June ! Children went in and out of its sunlight like bees ; the stones themselves of its seventeenth-century churches and palaces kept the taste of honey. At night, under a sky the lamps, not too strict, left in possession of the old squares, the darkness was open at both ends, on past and future. The children at least, looking at this future's clear profile, did not expect that it would turn to them the face of an enemy. How could they ? Their elders had brought them up to believe they had only to stretch their minds in the new schools, and exercise, in freedom, their easily strong bodies, to become a people the others would respect. They believed it. Nothing so youthfully candid could pretend to the happiness they gave off in the clear, the too clear and splendid light. It was almost palpable, this light, like the rind of a fruit. No thought of its bitter pulp crossed their minds. Their parents . . . these by now knew the truth, and remained calm. A people never behaved with a simpler dignity than these Czechs who knew they were living in the full shadow of a German conquest. True, as honest people they believed in the honesty of their friends : even their President, warned during these days by an Englishman in private talk not to trust too much in the English or his French ally, smilingly dismissed the warning. He, too, believed — if only in the self-interest of rich countries whose interests must surely, like his, push them against robbery with violence.

But the calm, and the strong confidence, went deeper, too deep for even treachery to reach. They are part of the inheritance of this people, in its wide valley of rivers, forests, mountains with lakes, lying between western and eastern Europe, seeded into by both, but harvesting only itself. And with what gross delicate vigour — as though the Renaissance had waited three centuries, buried in the earth here, a suave and smilingly perfect image, to be uncovered by the spades of the generation first free to excavate its own life.

How few gestures this young country, born to an old and obstinately strong family, has had time to make. Each of them in its assurance a curve towards a free and quietly human life. Land was given to the peasants, schools, very many schools, were built, and its children set to learn the use to the future of their hands and minds. Had the nation guessed how many of its new schools would serve as barracks for an invader, would it, during these twenty years, have tried as hard? I think so. Despair is not Czech.

A minor diplomat when I was in Prague complained to me that the Czechs are ill-bred. He was stupid enough to think that breeding is less an affair of endurance in the same place for centuries than of the tricks a man like himself, of poor intelligence, can learn easily in a few years. The Czechs, God be thanked, are not a charming people. (This same year I saw in Hungary what, when you reverse the coin, is profiled on charm.) In truth they are not unlike us English, before we were broken in : uncomfortably stubborn, fond of good food and drink, with a shrewd malice rolled under their tongues, gross, subtle, patient. Even now, when without (it seems) any aid other than the conscience of the world may give by groaning in its sleep, they are being left to the Germans, I find it impossible to believe that no adult future is to be given them. Especially when, after listening to that demented voice screaming from Berlin, I hear the quiet reasonable voice of Beneš. A Europe deaf to this voice is dying, and no help for it : those of us to whom she used to be a warm nurse will need to have ready the clean pennies for her eyes.

*

Prague, my newspaper says, is calm. Of course. . . .
The garden of the Ministry for Foreign Affairs, in the Černín

Palace, was noisy that evening with writers of a score of countries, chattering like — writers ; the English, like children, about each other, the French what always sounds like political arithmetic, and the other nations, with degrees of excitement rising to the simple fury of a Central European delegate describing his wife's recipe for hare soup, about literature, cooking, and affairs. My neighbour, a Czech, listened for a time with a serious smile.

" They are happy ? " she asked anxiously.

" Obviously. Writers when they are unhappy glare at each other and note down without wasting them in talk the clever phrases that come into their heads."

" Yes— " she laid on my arm a thin hand. Young, delicate, she had worn herself out preparing this writers' conference — " but will they go home liking us ? They've seen — they must — how hard we are working, so that no one shall be poor or ignorant, or ashamed. They'll be able, won't they ?, to contradict anyone who tells foolish lies about us. . . ."

" What are you hoping for ? " I asked.

After a minute she said softly,

" Nothing."

" Nothing ? "

The garden had not been lighted. With their total absence of vulgarity, the Czechs leave what is perfect alone. They knew that the seventeenth century and the lucent darkness of a June night should be left to form their own cool sun. Jiřina's face, pale from overwork, was hardly visible. I had to catch it reflected in her light voice. She was smiling.

" Don't mistake me, my darling— " in her innocence, after listening to the English, she had taken this word to mean " my friend " — " I know that none of you will tell lies. You will repeat that Prague is beautiful . . . it is . . . that everyone here is happy to be able to work madly for Czechoslovakia, that you learned one word of Czech, that we are kind, lively, and we eat a great deal of goose, and drink slivovitz. And nothing you say will have the slightest effect, because your Government has made its mind up already." Her voice ran out to a fine edge. " If only I knew what ! "

" It's impossible," I protested, " for us to let Germany defeat you. For our own sake. We are selfish, but not idiotic."

Jiřina patted my hand. "You are always good and clever," she said lightly. "I hope very much that all the governments have only good clever Ministers. I'm sure yours has. It is a pity" — her eyes sparkled — "that we have no concentration camps and don't make threatening speeches. Not one, not a single one of your statesmen has said we are a proud sensitive people and mustn't be provoked." Her voice trembled a little. "And how true. We are only stubborn and modest — and we are not afraid."

I remembered the way in which some of our politicians spoke of Beneš. I was silent. Jiřina looked at me to see what I was thinking, and I hurried to say, "You have a superb country."

"We shall keep it," she said quietly. . . .

It was Jiřina who sent out this appeal to the conscience of the world. I saw her hand, thin, small, fold it into the envelope, and the concentrated purpose of her body, as slight as a child's, without a single cowardly nerve. What will the Nazis do to her when they take her country?

*

The French writer Jules Romains, an orator and not simply a speaker, was addressing the conference. His rhetoric had been prepared with all that sense of responsibility a Frenchman feels towards syntax and verbal logic. It was gracefully ironical and witty. Towards Czechoslovakia its feelings were irreproachable. Here, you would say, is a writer, a Frenchman, who will defend with his last spasm of eloquence the country for which he feels this concern and respect, both deep. Behind a table the shortness of the speaker's body was not apparent; his head, large, with the delicately heavy features of a sculpture in wood, had the space he occupied almost to itself.

My fault of listening with, instead of my mind, an ear non-existent somewhere in my body, spoiled this speech for me. The generous phrases and avowals echoed in it doubtfully, as though, having to prepare so much, he had not given himself the trouble of attending to the echo. What is it, after all ? Only the mirror side of the voice. Looking at it, I saw reserves hidden like secret drawers in these charmingly turned sentences. A little nervously, I turned to glance at the Czech writers. Had they noticed ? No. They were delighted with him, sedate in their satisfaction.

Perhaps I was mistaken.

*

The other bank here of the Danube had been Austrian and was now, only since March, in Germany. After a time we came to a place, the meeting of two rivers, where a German and a Slovak village faced each other across the stream. They were a village and its reflection in a mirror : here, on this side, the low houses, whitewashed, and deep roofs, the trees and shabby wooden palings, the fresh greenness of water-meadows, leaned quietly and saw itself in its image *there*. Even the black horse near us threw its thinner reflection into the other field. The river's surface was doubled and self-reflective, wind flowing one way and water another, itself the mirror between the two villages, and ignorant — which was which ? If war breaks out, one of them will be forced to obliterate the other. Afterwards, when it steps up to the glass to look at itself, it will see what ? Sterility, absence. . . . What kind of people are we, who hold a child up to a mirror to watch it smile at itself — and then, its half-closed skull the tool, smash life and likeness ?

And now I remember the German woman who came out of her house to the edge of the stream and stood there, arms hanging as if she had forgotten them, stood, and looked into the Slovak village. When I was a child I looked in the same way into the mirror between the windows, not to see myself, but trying to see the other, to follow her when she turned her back and began to live among the same things another life, free, no adults with raised voices or a stick, quietly alone with her sole plays, a life turned widely endlessly out, always out.

*

I have begun a second book. The difficulty of writing two at once is less than the boredom of writing always the same one. No doubt it will break down ; one or the other will insist on undivided attention, but for a few weeks at least I can carry both. It is exhausting, and that alone would be worth the labour.

War now seems certain. Yesterday, when I was listening to the broadcast of Hitler's speech in that absurd Sport-Palast, I made a discovery. In spite of the hatred in his voice, piercing what slight defence our entrails can make against a sound so pitched, there is less in it of pure evil than in Goebbels's. These disembodied voices give away the secrets of their bodies. I could not listen to Goebbels, who spoke first, without growing horror. The skin of my head felt as though it were being peeled off, exposing the flayed brain and nerves. Who, looking back — if our descendants are able to look at anything but their road — will understand why we gave these men power over us ? Or will forgive us our treachery ? (It will need an anatomist to lay it bare.)

In this, as I suppose in other towns, we have been fitting gas-masks. I saw a child's face, in the instant before it was seized by the mask, suddenly invaded by fear, the blood driven out and all the veins choked by his anguish : he sat stiffly, hand gripping his thin knee. His mother, young and shabby, watched him, ashamed to speak, ashamed even to touch him, with so many people looking. I saw them going away afterwards, hand in hand, carrying their masks. . . .

A man who knows him said to me about Neville Chamberlain that he " is not inhuman but he lacks imagination ". What if his imagination were bounded — on one side — by the so quickly broken bodies of children ? Nowadays when we fight for what we believe in, we hold out to the bomb which will split it open just such a child, helpless in our hands. What is to be done ? Step by step, older men who are not inhuman have led us to this room with the desks, the maps and children's drawings pinned on the walls, where instead of learning a child sits and is tortured. Which of them dare I blame ? All these years, the horror of war has been stretched across my eyes, a bandage, not a lens. Who will forgive us our blind gestures as war came ? My little child, it is I, your mother, who is drawing the wire through your brain and filling your mouth with dust.

The door-bell rang. I answered it and signed my sister's name for three gas-masks, one of them a child's. "And the baby," I asked, "the little girl?"

"A blanket can be wrapped round her and she can be carried to the nearest gas-shelter."

"Oh. Where is it?"

A nervous smile. "There isn't one."

*

The first inoculation not having taken, the Czechoslovak writers tried again. This time it was brief. Perhaps the vein they were drawing on for the serum had closed.

> *Prague, 30th September, 1938*
>
> ### To the Conscience of the World
>
> *On this day when, by the decision of four statesmen, our country has been abandoned and delivered to injustice, with its hands bound, we remember your declarations of friendship, in the sincerity of which we believe. . . . Sacrificed, but not conquered, we charge you, who for the present have escaped our lot, to persevere in the common struggle of mankind.*

I folded it away and with it the memories which otherwise might have lain about and got lost. Not all of these need looking after. A great many of them are out of the reach of a merely human memory. Such is Hradčany, lifted above sleeping Prague in a light thin enough to seem worn by time. Its absence, if it were destroyed by bombs, would be the form into which, for the sake of longer life, it had changed. There are others, among them Jiřina, for whom my skull is a thin cup, holding a very little life. During these last months she has written three times, letters so full of her eager spirit there is no room in them for bitterness or doubts. The third and last was a postcard, showing a narrow window closed by a grill of Renaissance iron-work; in the room behind it, one lamp. Since then, nothing.

*

In the train this evening I tried to read a poet. He had to

94

struggle, poor wretch, with only my weak help, against the other people in the carriage. They had musical instruments of some sort on the rack. One, tall and stout, was a Jew ; with him were a short fat man in an enormous overcoat protecting all of him except his head and feet, and a negro with one peg-top leg : clipped to it, the striped trouser-leg of a morning suit. The leader was the short man : facing him, the Jew learned aloud verses beginning : The Gollies are having a party, the Gollies are having fun. He had so much trouble in memorising it that the repetitions formed behind him a landscape, unchanging for an hour, the street with the fun palace, youths and girls fumbling their pennies into the slot, slack-fingered, half-ashamed. the shops offering a drug guaranteed to cure both impotence and fertility, the Odeon selling cheap illusions at so much the living-hour, torn newspapers, the stale air which by now is only the breath of all these unclean bodies and of what they eat and excrete : all today's dear pleasures. Every few minutes the leader snatched the page from his hands and " heard " him. He was anxious. " You gotter be word perfect. The spotlight is on you. Yes, yes, you know it, but you're thinking. You mustn't think." This went on and on, and the Poet triumphed ! Not easily, but he triumphed. He was stronger, more solid and wiry, than many writers who show off their useless muscles. Of all poets the least able to bear the street coming into his house, waiting in an attentive anguish until the space of an obscure room gave birth to exotic voyages, until a lamp figured agony, a fan ecstasy and flight, he was still stronger than this cacophony of the present. The sunset on the left of the train was his favourite hour : in just such a flat green country, the curve of the river, a girl's arm throwing off a white shift, her nakedness, the absent swan, merged into a single musical phrase, each of its notes containing all the others. Indoors again, the sunset reflects itself in a mirror, the only living gesture, and fixed, of a mind nailed to the Absolute. A modesty not to be distinguished from extreme pride closed for him every door leading to the life he could quite easily have led, in which a high reputation would have attached to work falling a degree or less short of his ideal. *Je vague peu, préférant à tout, dans un appartement défendu par la famille, le séjour parmi quelques meubles anciens et chers et la feuille de papier souvent blanche.* Movement, apparently motionless, towards a limpid purity reflecting all the errors of life. Even the three jazz musicians ?

*

Vienna 19, Paradisgasse.

My friends have lived in this house for a great number of years. Since it held a large family it is of fair size — but modest, even a little shabby : at the back its wooden verandah looks over a neglected garden, admirable for children. And since they are Jews, they will not be allowed to live here much longer. A Nazi official called yesterday and looked over it. Already one of the daughters, the most brilliant, is in Palestine and the tall young son on his way there. The other daughters, candid and lively, the youngest so gay, must go. They have had one alarm, when suddenly they were taken away to clean the Nazi barracks. Their mother implored to be taken instead. The young storm-trooper, almost a boy, looked at her and said, with simplicity, "But of course they must come. Would *you* let your mother go in your place ?" It was clear he would have been shocked if the girls had shown such a lack of affection and respect.

Before any harm came to them at the barracks they were sent home. The woman who had been a servant in the house, until the order forbidding Aryans to work for Jews, ran as soon as she heard about it to the barracks, and raged and scolded — it takes a good deal to silence an angry Viennese working-woman — until she got her way.

But the parents ? How much Vienna means to them ! How they are held to it by all the deeds and thoughts of a quietly long married life, and of the childhood from which almost without interval they passed into being husband and wife. The thoughts and voices of their great-great-grandparents reach out from the dark streets close to the Danube, to clutch and draw them. How become deaf to all this, and to the voices of old cups, of chairs polished during a lifetime, of worn fine linen ? In the end they will decide to go with their children, and Vienna will be the poorer by a retired professor of history and his wife.

Don't you see ? Their goodness, simple without naïveté, has
a loyal radiance, and Vienna is no longer so full of light that
it can afford to lose it. It cannot, but it will : it will lose the
serenity of Anna's smiling mouth, a young moment cancelling
the grief, older than she is, of her eyes ; it will lose the love
she pours over so many of its commonest things, reviving them ;
her body, which still keeps its angular girlhood ; her mind,
sheltering in the very centre of its experience an essential innocence. She has no supple or caressing softness : all her acts
are purely direct and simple, the direct movements of a spirit.
What, when she goes, will happen to the things in her house
which she has served carefully all her life because it was a way
of serving her parents, who also had used them, and her children ?
To the cup she is turning in her fingers ? "Look, it was my
mother's," she says, smiling.

Who will drink from it in future — and what, in Nazi
Vienna, will he drink ?

*

Some of the many Jews in Vienna, less courageous, or closer
menaced than my friends, have not waited. Either they had no
hope of escape, or the end, when they thought of holding out,
was too heavy for them to carry. They snatched themselves
from it, some violently ; but one at least whom I knew gave
himself poison in a cup such as Anna had shown me, his name-
day cup, given him when he was an infant ; perhaps he felt,
because it had always been in the house, that it was still friendly.

Others are trying to escape. They fill the courtyard and
rooms of our Consulate, pressed closely together, jostling each
other for a foothold on the stairs, clamorous or silent, patient,
raging. Their faces all have the same habit : at moments they
become quite vacant, as though the life behind them sank
down, unable to drag itself another step ; then in a minute it
remembers and starts up, and sweat breaks out on the yellowish
skin, or the lips tremble and a drop of moisture forms there
and hangs. There is an extraordinary odour, making it difficult
to breathe in the rooms. I have never smelled it before, and
I recognise it — the smell of fear. The harassed consular staff
does its best ; it is forced to keep the door locked on the inner

courtyard, letting in two or three at a time the crowd which surges forward, all at once, crying, imploring life, as soon as the door opens. If I hold my passport up above the heads of these frantic shades, I shall be let in ahead of them. For a long time I cannot make myself do this. Why remind the others that one of us here is still alive ?

Some of these men and women come here day after day and stand. They are losing their hold on time, on the time they knew. When after hours of waiting they realise that the door is closing for the last time they do not feel that a day has passed. Each of them now is increasingly alone : his mind has ceased to remind him, not only about the passage of hours and days, but that these walls, these stones and stone steps, look to other people as they do to him. Knee deep in it like animals in a stream, each is living closed in a single world of feeling — heat, hunger, or the trembling of his limbs. See, they don't talk to each other : at first they did, taking out a hope or a terror and handing it round. What could they say now when none of them sees anything except his fear ? All he hears or touches is only this sensation of fear, which belongs blindly to him, not to any of the others. The world now is only what he feels. He is his fear.

A woman who has been leaning against the wall, with both hands on it, faints. They look at her lying there in her black clothes, and at first no one moves. At last and sullenly, three men lift her and carry her outside. What if in their absence the door opens again for a minute ? And against the other wall a child sitting on the ground plays, tired of it, with a small wooden horse. Continually he lifts his eyes to look at his mother standing above him. She, pale, and like the others alone, has ceased to answer his look, and he turns it again to the toy which long since stopped caring for him.

*

Today it rained, a chill fine rain which clings like cobwebs. Why am I in Vienna, if all I speak to turns out to be the husk of something I expected to find alive — the park now almost a barracks, the friendly owner of the Keller become slyly a

Nazi ? I felt restless and ashamed this morning. I walked about the streets, between the Kärntner Strasse and the Graben, to and fro endlessly : I had forgotten what I was looking for until, very suddenly, I stumbled on it. It came abruptly and gently out of the Vienna of eight years ago ; and gave itself up — one of those moments, unwilled, unbidden except by the cry in us we did not even know was waiting and with all its force expectant, when the whole of a past, of one of our pasts, opens itself in the present. It lives, we say, again. What nonsense ! Its new life is no more like the old than my hand, with eight more years of work marked on it, is the hand I brought here in 1930. The endless moment this morning when I stood and brushed the rain from my face in front of an obscure shop in a narrow unpromising side-street, had had dissolved into it an infinity of moments. They cannot be counted because I can't separate them. There are all those when as a child I was saving my pocket-money — a weekly threepence — against the next birthday or Easter or Christmas or the anniversary of her wedding or New Year : it was no use for her children to think of giving my mother a present which was not fine or unusual ; common things did not please her and she never pretended they did. And when I grew up, in every new or foreign place I visited, I searched the shops for the right present to take back to her. It was less habit than an instinctive will. Where the child, pretending an interest, had stood and stared into foreign shops, the grown woman, alone now, stared thinking : Would it do for her ? Would she like it ? If ever my whole self acted, it did when it looked for presents for her — as it does now when I give things to my only son or my young sister. And perhaps only then.

When I was here before, it was very hot. I looked a long time at handbags in the window now covered with anti-Jewish notices, but day after blazing day passed before I could make up my mind. I walked about, giving her this dress and that bag, giving her the milky Danube looked down on from the Kahlenberg, giving her the Opera House and Jeritza's clear voice of light and triumph, but it was not until the moment in front of this shop, accidentally reached — not a street where you would expect such a shop — that I saw her present : the curiously

woven bed-jacket in white soft wool, almost weightless, a feather
lying on my hand. Could I, when I was buying it, know that
she would admire it so much she would grow afraid to wear it ?
It spent almost all its time with her between layers of soft paper.
Or that the moment, nearer than all the others, and part of them,
inseparable, which would give to this latest its form and colour
— springing from the bitterest depth, the gentlest shadow, of
my life as daughter and human being, stifling me — of a tear,
would be the one when I handed it to the two women who
were dressing her ? " She liked this, it's almost new, let her
wear it."

*

There is no way, in words, to express these moments formed
from a lifetime of others. It can be done in music, where without
effort the ear takes in a whole world of experience dissolved
note by note in a single phrase. The poet who came nearest
to it, in certain of his poems, did not succeed. Offered one of
his condensed and complex images — and when their sense is
most musical their sound is often least so — we cannot help
separating the several images, to set them side by side for the
benefit of a false clearness, and thus all but destroy them before
reviving them by plunging them again into the verse.

> *Mais langoureusement longe*
> *Comme de blanc linge ôté*
> *Tel fugace oiseau si plonge*
> *Exultatrice à côté*
>
> *Dans l'onde toi devenue*
> *Ta jubilation nue.*

Even in the verse the words are hard and definite, more images
than evocative. Evocation may be strongest when the objects
it names are least clear.

And since he, of all poets, failed, it seems that there is no
direct way, by means of words, to express the only realities of
our life. We live, apart from these few scattered moments,
wholly on the unreal surface, joined by words to things and
creatures about whom we know nothing except in the moments
we cannot share with them. Extreme and unendurable —

except that we endure it — silence of our life. The only words we find are lies. The mind speaks no language, and language offers only symbols of mind. Sometimes, not often, we act the truth. But here, too, it is perhaps only the last minute which is true, when it is out of our hands to make a deceitful or false gesture.

*

Remembering it — and the rain had stopped — I went through the other courtyards into the Josefs-Platz. It was empty, except for an elderly man who was standing as if puzzled : he might have forgotten why he had come. Looking at him a little closely I saw that he was a Jew. I walked across the small square, my back to its shuttered windows of the Pallavicini palace, followed by them, to the place where in 1930 a few rows of chairs faced a platform in the angle of the Redouten-Säle and the great Library. It was dark then, the dark warmth of a June night. There were no lights except in a few windows, and one on the platform for the singers. Behind the chairs occupied for the most part by foreigners with money to spend, the small crowd of Viennese people, a few of them barefoot, shadows and unmoving in the darkness. I stood now in the full sunlight and asked for the darkness. It came only for a second, and in the Pallavicini building behind me windows opened in rooms where a lamp turned down scarcely showed a single or two or three listening figures, and the last note of the Nacht-musik reached across eight years to die in the sunlight, in the empty square. Empty ? The elderly Jew was there — listening — or only seeing. Hardly likely that his silence was the same shape and colour as mine, but like mine it filled the square, between the windows, and as far upwards as we chose to think. And no doubt for him, too, nothing as he waited happened, except perhaps the silence itself, the refusal to answer, the stubborn absence of the dead when we speak ; the waiting, the doubts, the remembered moment where the darkness will be reflected, and when as now we neither hear nor speak.

*

It is good to look back sometimes, and notice how great

joy or great despair alike told us nothing, absolutely nothing. I was fourteen when we moved into a new house. I can see myself cutting up a loaf at a table in the window of the kitchen : such a large room, and full of air and brightness. Outside I could hear children playing in a garden, and a poignant delicious joy seized me, with the thought of living here, mixed somehow with the smell of the new bread I was buttering, and the idea of new friends. Nothing warned me of the despair these children would make me suffer by jeering at my awkwardness. Nor, when I was suffering the agony of being laughed at, could I imagine — and be comforted — a time when they would be exemplary men and women, about whom I should not even know whether they are living or dead.

*

Budapest.

The delight of solitude in a foreign town. I felt it as soon as I woke this morning. No one here knows me, I shall speak to no one, except concierges and waiters, I am free — and always under my eyes, I have only to go to the window, less cloudy, brighter and colder than in Vienna, and a part of the life here, the Danube. This feeling of freedom, of my real and own life stretching itself in me, realising that it is free to feel, think, be what it please, is extraordinary — and worth a great deal.

And what is this own life ? Let me look at you. Come ; come forward from whatever it is you hide in, an old blackened, with age, mirror, or a lie or many lies. No one is here. Even the room doesn't know you, has never seen us, and will forget us the moment we have gone. In any event, and however long you live in it, you never manage to impress a room. Outside, a foreign city, indifferent, with its secrets you may guess but needn't acknowledge, is waiting : you can walk in it without being seen. Well ? Nothing, I see, expansive or reckless : a rather cold curiosity ; an eye, an ear ; self-absorbed, shut-in. There is more in you than I thought of the old kind of captain, the man who carries all the responsibility for his ship and the authority, so that he is deeply and for months alone and can never give himself away, and if to begin with he were reserved or felt slighted, he has become secretive, surly, hard. It is when you are alone in a foreign country that you behave like him, and are more like him than you are like her, the captain's young wife who only needed company to walk about staring openly and wondering. This morning it is as if a drop of the North Sea had found itself in Central Europe. Would it change its nature ? No — it would become itself, completely, coolly, joyously itself — if joy is this feeling of space round what has been squeezed and twisted.

My great-grandfather's name, common in that narrow edge of north-east England, was the first I saw written on a house-door in Norway. But the coast town, small, quiet, in those days isolated and sound, not yet thumb-marked by vulgar wishes, where I was born and lived — yes, that at least was a life — was a Danish settlement, built over the charred wood of the huts they burned when they landed from their long ships. My remote ancestors then were Danes, and no very pleasant people. Nearer at hand, my father, a master mariner, my mother daughter of a shipowner, kept a certain coldness and harshness, not always in reserve. As for me, I am polite, deceitful, warm-hearted, cold, unfeeling, betrayed by my strong feelings, placid, cat-nervous, etc. etc. A proper Northman.

*

Budapest stinks of violence and death. I almost believe that behind this façade of deep quick-flowing river, dolomitic hill, palace, superb street fronting the Danube, restlessly crowded cafés, is a vent from the cruelty rising in Europe. Abominably, the stones exude the smell of cruelty and violence. Nowhere else, not even in the Vienna I left yesterday, is it so much part of the air, bright, massive, of July, one breathes. Yet I do not feel that it is this town which will be murdered ; nor that it is exhausted — there are seeds in this Danube country. It is more as if all the fresh cruelties gathering first in Berlin, then in Vienna, tomorrow where ? in Prague ?, had collected here in a stale stagnant pool. Strange — and not frightening. The blind creature in me, groping, which touches something wet under its fingers feeling along the wall, tastes it, and finds it salt and warm, may be afraid, but I don't feel her trembling. Why need I ? A shadow has nothing to be afraid of. What am I in Budapest except the farthest edge of a shadow, thrown by a life rooted at the other side of a continent and a cold sea ?

There is no mistaking what it is one smells here — nor the after-taste of the finest bread I have ever eaten. Your perfect bread, my dear and handsome city, your admirable strong coffee, have the taste, when they have been swallowed, of cruelty and hatred.

How is it that I recognise it so quickly ?

*

Each time I cross the courtyard, the wife of the porter makes friendly signs from her doorstep. She is a big woman, shapeless : her broad face with its high cheek-bones and dark narrow eyes, has been worn to a curious smoothness by life ; her lips fold with a cynical good-humour all the secrets, discreditable to them, she keeps about other people. Nothing now will surprise her, not even an act of goodness and self-sacrifice. She refuses to quarrel with her bad-tempered husband : not that she has any fear of him, but her warm lazy blood has turned in her to a tolerance so lax that it is not even a virtue. Yesterday I saw her sitting, hands in her lap, looking across the river to Pest. Her smile, the soft amplitude of her body, were waiting calmly for anything the sewer-vent pours out. Nothing, unless it harms her family, can disturb them. When I was talking to her, in the sign language we use — she has a vocabulary of signs springing from her endlessly : a movement of her thumb, casual but deep image of her life, says infinitely more than a volley of words rebounding from its surface — a thin pregnant cat jumped on to her lap. Her fingers exploring, stroking its body, she talked to it in thick sly glances, sharing with it and me some appalling joke about our habit of conceiving and giving birth. Then with an effort — she had a few words of French — she said, " Je crois — quatre et pour cette nuit — " in a voice which set in motion all the notes of a chord and abruptly muted them. This morning when I came downstairs she was waiting for me in the yard. In one hand she held the stick she uses to wash clothes. She held up four fingers of the other, then covered her eyes, smiling ; and slowly, like a Fate, poked the stick downwards four times.

*

She has two children, and indulges them as if they were grown up, only smiling when they behave badly. This being so, how am I to explain what I have just seen with my own eyes — or I would not believe ? The little girl was playing in the open door of their room, springing and crouching with one arm stretched out. Her hand suddenly caught and swept on to the floor a cup which fell in pieces. The blood ran to her face. She was rigid for a moment, then with a movement as quick as the thought she pushed her brother, still almost a baby, and made him sit on the floor near the broken cup, giving him a stick to hold. She was barely in time. Her mother came back into the room, lifted the infant, and began with her laugh shaking her body to caress and scold him.

The other child as she watched was half sullen, half betrayed by her curiosity. Clearly she was still held fast by the moment in which her body and mind had acted together like an animal. But why the act ? Where did the impulse come from ? Her mother would have laughed at the accident. Vanity ? Pride, was it ? In a little girl of four ? Or must I find treachery among our roots ? But treachery is surely fear ? — of what ? . . . Suddenly, from the most obscure depths of my own life, a confused image of myself, my own brother, and some childish betrayal. The first ? Probably not.

Two men who were crossing the courtyard had seen. They laughed, and one nudged the other. It was clear that they were seeing a quite different event from the one I had watched . . . and seen in it myself. And yet not seen. I can't go back over the road I came by ; I can't reach to or remember the first tiny movement of fear and treachery, turning in the same instant to cruelty. And I have never moved away from it and cannot escape.

I walked, half closing my eyes in the warm heavy light, out of the courtyard, and looked for a place still in shadow where

I could stand a minute. For some reason I found it an effort to breathe. Something, which has been growing in me since I was a child, with every breath, drawing its sap from all the veins and nerves of my life, had broken suddenly into a new and quite monstrous flower. It choked me. I felt it pushing against the roots of my eyes, tongue, nostrils. All the earlier and greener shoots of this tree of fear — the fear of being whipped, fear of losing or of being lost, of mockery, failure, of death, and the fear, until now seeming their only and sterile seed, of war — pressed up into this stifling growth. Their ferment rose in it ; they had only, in their several shapes, prefigured it ; perhaps each stamen of the new flower was one of them : but it was not like them, it had scarcely sprung up and I felt that it had always been there and like itself. I might turn to look at any moment of a past not my own, become any of the dead women in me — I should still be stifled by the feeling born in my mind this moment.

It occurred to me as I stood with my hand on the low wall that I could be killed by it. I made a movement to turn away. It was slight, almost unnoticeable, but I had made it, in the so brief instant when the image came into my mind of the café where with a newspaper — doubtfully, the waiter would offer me first the German papers, then the single French one he had — and cups of coffee with cream, I should spend the morning.

I had no idea where it would lead. Have I evaded something or accepted ? All I know, and without words, is that a climax has been reached, and a decision — to accept or turn aside — taken. Which ?

The stones, under my hand, were warm.

*

Though I have come so far, it is not to escape. In the middle years you can't : life takes up less and less room and the past more, in the glass the traveller carries, one glass holding both. This morning I was drinking my coffee in the shabby café near the Francis-Joseph bridge when the church bells began to ring in English. At once, behind, under, over them the bells rang of the Parish Church of St. Mary in the air thinner and clearer than this, and a hundred and ninety-nine steps led from the harbour to the top of the cliff; my mother and I climbed them, slowly, turning half-way to look down at the harbour and the roofs, and up towards the church on the cliff edge, its roof (made by ships' carpenters) and windows like the windows of cabins, the stone ship with its full cargo. The colour of this July sky paled, the air was filled with light flung back from the absent sea, it widened and flew upward with the gulls; without my willing it or hoping for it — I was not asked — the North Sea flowed over the waters of the Danube, bringing seaweed to mark the tide. Her life is not continued, except for this phantom always out of reach, in mine which flows back through hers : I am not always sure which past I am touching. The endless summer days between cliff and sea are mine, the Grass of Parnassus is mine, and the return, shoes heavy with sand, mine. But the dyed Easter eggs, red, yellow, purple, and the voice echoing in the room with three windows — O *dem golden slippers*, and *The Spanish cavalier sat under a tree . . . and if I should fall . . . fell for my co-un-tree and thee, love . . .*? What young woman stands in the frosty darkness pointing out to a child the magnificence of the Christmas shops, such small shops and glorious in their tinsel, and whose is this child's heart excited by the miracle? The shuttlecock is mine, and it was I who copied and painted birds from the great bird book on to ostrich eggs, the smooth coarse surface warmed by my hand. But the tunes worn so thin they are almost tuneless? Hers, but who gave them to her? And whose, brought by this tide chilling silently the Danube, is this deep unappeased grief?

It is better not to go back, but to remember as it was the path along the top of the cliff — see, there are no houses like a mouth full of rotten teeth opening in the fields, there is only the springing turf at the edge, or the hay drying, and in May the bushes of yellow broom. . . . I am going to get you some. You will hold it with the absorbed pleasure you take from a beautiful thing, as though you are giving yourself a reward for having so long put up with what you knew was poor. . . . Here is the road to the pier — don't say : Where are the mooring-posts? or notice what has eaten away the

face of the pier houses. That tall old building has become —
what you see. But, if I take you, you will come at the head of
the stone staircase to the long wide room filled with books,
with many windows, each with a table for readers, which look
over the lower harbour, over the masts of boats, to the Parish
Church : as you see, the librarian has a pulpit very like the
pulpit of a church, and on cool days the fireplace holds a good
fire where the oldest subscribers can sit to warm their hands ;
the rest must warm them at the books. A child is taking out
the first Jungle Book and an old man three volumes of Froude.
Don't look any longer : I may not be able to keep the mirror
empty for these to reflect in it — see, their breath clouds it —
nor the quietness brushing with a gloved hand the edges of the
shelves. And do not try, when you leave, to buy jet — it is
paltry stuff now — until I have shown you what fine work
filled these shops you can see only if you keep closely behind
my eyes. I'll take you further, to the toyshop not there, the
small rooms honeycombed with shelves and every shelf crammed
with toys, the cell-like drawers dripping toys, the rows of dolls'
heads, the hoops and skipping-ropes, and the beads for threading.
The child touches them, and walks quickly up the steep staircase
to the vanished upper room, then down into the narrow street,
in the half-dark where the light crosses the light from the
past.

Images follow the exile because no one else would trouble to
keep them. Who else wants a wooden paling, covered by wind-
beaten briars ? Or would rather sit, shivering a little, in the
cool north-east summer evening, listening to music played out
of doors from an open bandstand, than covered in by walls
sit thigh by thigh with other degenerates ?

Is it only now, here, in Central Europe waiting to flow back
when the bell stops, that I have you ? Only when, the Danube
becoming the North Sea, life becomes all memory ? And all,
all, the streets, the sea-weathered wood, the toys, the sand under
the bare feet, lead to the same figure, the same voice under the
voices, the same, and endlessly broken, silence. Which of us
takes the steep street from the bridge, you who died and are
now living, or I your still living child who is dead ? Neither of

us makes a sound, neither is noticed — except by this cool light darkening the roofs, and this horizon the colour of the sea.

*

When I was young I used to tell the others endless fairy tales. The price to them was three deeds a day. They did, three times, what I asked them. In return, I continued the saga. Quite suddenly I lost the knack. That must have been when I began reading the novels which came into the house, four or five a week : my mother glanced through them and sent them back ; it was I who read them. How stupid parents are. If they must read the popular novels of their day, why can't they at least keep them from their children as carefully as they would any other poison ?

Today it was very hot. I sat — as always drinking more coffee than I should : after the second or third cup my heart beats frantically, like a metronome ; I rather enjoy the sensation — drowsily, at the iron table, and watched the Danube moving, grey, massive, between its walls. It covers up its secrets — from the days when children were sacrificed to it as a god until now when last night's suicide disappears as quickly as all those Jewish bodies, old and young, tumbled into it a few years ago. The sun's paw, covered by cloud, was quite murderous this morning ; I felt it drawn through my flesh to the nerves. I was almost asleep and did not at first realise that I was telling myself one of those forgotten tales. This is it, as I wrote it on the dingy sheet of paper the waiter gave me from his pocket.

It began with a girl, naturally a princess, sleeping in the garden where she had lived all her life. It was a charming garden, half forest, half smooth turf divided by a stream. The princess smiled in her sleep, and one tear rolled down her cheek, only one. When she woke she began to spin and weave — the usual life of a princess in these circumstances. But this morning an accident happened, the usual accident. Her bobbin sprang from her fingers and rolled quickly away into the deep forest ; she ran after it for hours, and not until darkness fell did she realise she was lost, the trees closed round her, there was no path : she sank down weeping on a rock and slept. She awoke in the half-light before day and caught a glimpse of animals and birds disappearing among the trees, then the sun rose and she stretched herself and saw fruit hanging from the branch nearest her. Pulling one, she broke it open, it was full of juice and pulp, so bitter it set her teeth on edge, but she ate it and felt better. Now she saw beyond the trees a poor sort of house. She went to it and knocked, and found that a baker lived here with his wife and their son, a pleasant young man, except that he had a slight squint. They asked her if she were willing to work : when she agreed they took her in at once. The work was much harder than weaving had been, but she did her best. Only, every day she stole a little of the baker's dough, and kneaded it into three tiny figures she baked in a dark corner of the oven. In the evening when she was alone in her attic she pricked her finger and let a drop of the blood fall on each. Then they came alive and would answer questions, until she asked how she could get home. At that they were silent.

All this giving away drops of her blood began to tell on her. She grew pale, and nothing did her any good. One evening the son, who suspected she was up to some trick or other, looked through a crack in her door and saw her talking to the loaf-images. Next day he asked her to marry him and give up this dangerous habit. In spite of his squint he was really very handsome, and she did not dislike him. She promised to think it over. That evening she made only one image, the image of a child, and asked it, " Shall I marry him ? " The image replied, " Yes, certainly, if you want to begin what will always repeat itself. Your child will have a child and she will have children and so on for ever. Is that life ? " The princess shuddered. " No," she cried, " you shan't any of you live," and in her anger she broke the image and threw the pieces behind the rafters. She waited until all in the house were asleep, then slipped out and ran through the forest as far as she could, only stopping when she was worn out. Without knowing why — was it the thought of the young man with the squint and the grey eyes ? — she began to weep. From her tears sprang a stream flowing down hill among the roots of trees ; she followed it in the darkness, lower, lower, half thinking she knew it. It was something she should have expected. The sun rose and in the new light she saw in front of her a landscape so charming she would have thought it a painting if the bees had not shaken the flowers they sucked. And then her eyes opened in a still brighter daylight, she recognised her garden, which looked at her as if it knew her, and she saw she was lying in her bed of gold and marble, looking at the sky, her hands folded — the way a princess should sleep. The light pressed on her eyelids so heavily that she fell asleep, smiling and weeping one tear. It was as clear as glass ; if you had looked into it you would have seen the baker's kitchen, the young squinting man, and the child's child's child. As the old women say, one can't have all of everything.

*

I met a German woman today, in a house in one of the secretive streets behind the Margit-rakpart. She is here on an undefined mission — she said she was studying child welfare.

" Here ? " I said. " In Hungary ? "

I told her what I had seen in the railway station. I heard a pattering of tiny hooves, the sound made by goats on a hard track. Turning my head, I saw a score of women, peasants, each carrying her belongings in a small bundle, being herded along the platform by an elderly man in shabby black. It was their bare feet as they scurried past had made the sound. Framed in dry yellow hair, their faces reflected nothing they looked at, none of the bustling objects of a main station. A little boy followed one of them closely. Running on brown sticks of legs, he tried to touch her with his claw, but she was always out of reach, as if she had forgotten him ; there was room between her skirt and his hand for a wave of fear to lift itself and rush down on him. He met shock after cold shock, his eyelids kept closing, then stretching again in an attempt to see her and beyond her some place where they would rest. If I could have taken this look of his and placed it in front of the people who decide what is to be done with harvests, surely one of them would have recognised it and been ashamed ?

" Why not admit," she said, " that none of these countries

is fit to govern itself? When we govern them things will be better. We don't ill-treat our servants."

"Please tell me what you mean," I said.

She had a broad charming face, simple and intelligent. "There are servant races. All the trouble in the world comes from not recognising this one truth. Why should you believe that life created only one sort of human being although it created so many sorts of insects and animals? Clearly in some races, the first impulse, the *élan vital*, weakened or turned back. All these minor European nations — there is nothing to be done except train and use them. They are not experiments, they are unfinished impulses, ideas, contradictions — as if nature had scattered the qualities of a great man and waited to see which impulse would absorb the others and become the man destined to rule the planet. It is after all such a small planet. One pair of hands. . . ."

Hers were short-fingered and white. She moved them as if she were throwing a ball.

"And that is the German?"

"You English came nearest to us," she said, smiling, "but your evolution stopped short of producing the greatly privileged man, the leader who is a genius. It is to us he was born."

If she had been anything but a good gently-spoken creature, I should not have been shocked. And there was a logic in what she said — it is true that one reason why I have failed is that I did not refuse all but one of my selves : they were so many and they all wanted to be given life. But with an anger I could not soften I rejected her logic. Nations are not selves to be nursed or destroyed. They have each their sap rising from the silent voices of their roots, through their memories, to the newest bud — *Cette petite espérance qui n'a l'air de rien du tout. Cette petite fille espérance. Immortelle.* . . . I was going to speak when our hostess came back into the room, and the German who had just condemned her to servitude turned to this young Hungarian woman, a painter, and said tenderly,

"And your pictures, my dear Mária, you are going to show us your wonderful wonderful paintings?"

*

1939
Royan, July 2.

A few discreet posters announced that this evening, Sunday, the Musique Municipale de Saumur would play at Royan " sous la direction de Monsieur Bienvenu ". I went to listen. It was scarcely dark, and in the clear and deceitful light the sky spread into the sea dove-like dunes of cloud. People sauntered between the open bandstand — there were no lights except a few round the edge of its roof — and the trees. I caught sight of the headlines in a copy of *L'Œuvre* — La situation générale demeure très sérieuse. The man reading it said suddenly, " No," — looking at the ground and speaking to himself.

Walking towards the bandstand, I had to cross a stretch of sandy gravel. At once, and before I could draw back, I was walking on one of the paths leading, along the side of the cliff, through the rough enclosure called then the Saloon, down towards the band playing on the terrace cut out halfway between the top of the cliff and the shore. Here, looking across the sea, my mother and I listened evening after summer evening to the gently prancing music proper to a small half-forgotten town balancing at the edge of the sea. How charming it was, and how dull and the colour of a young breeze. And alas, vanished, under the unhappy changes which overtook it in its gradual metamorphosis into a Spa, never to be seen again by anyone until the sound of the gravel under my foot joined with the lightly salt air and the absence of any comfort or fuss round this Saumur band to give it back " under the direction of M. Bienvenu " — yes, yes, you are welcome, my Saloon, in your reserved simplicity, in the discomfort of your benches without shelter, your shabby theatre where no play more daring than an early Pinero was ever seen, your ghosts holding their skirts from the dust, and children with long loose hair. I trembled with happiness, in the certainty that never, never so long as I live, nor perhaps after that, will a foolish town council improve you for the benefit of strangers who ought not to have been pandered to. Moreover, you are mine. The suave light falling round you comes through my eyes. No use for you to hide again behind the changes scrawled over you ; you will come now when I choose, awkward, shabby, gay, firmly in that moment, out of all my moments, I give you. The fatigue, the anxiety, I had been feeling, vanished. For a minute I felt, as I used to feel then, that I could do anything, anything.

I feel at home in this French crowd. Nowhere in Europe do people dress worse or less pretentiously than the provincial French, and there is no people I respect more. Respect, not like. They present to liking a smooth impermeable surface, on which not even a fly could cling. But how many qualities one sees playing behind this, to the foreigner, impassable barrier — a simplicity, which does not exclude shrewdness and malice, a refusal to be bled in spirit or money for the sake of show, a stubborn self-will living easily under cover of their terrible *respect humain* : each Frenchman cultivates his soul as jealously as we used to grow aspidistras, with a sharp eye for its difference from his neighbours'. I bear them, since they are at home, no grudge for their involuntary contempt for foreigners. It will never lead them to interfere — and it reminds me of those violent greedy eccentrics, my ancestors. But these French people play. With their ideas, emotions, bodies. You only have to watch elderly men talking or young men and girls amusing themselves on the sands with a child's ball. It is a habit we have almost lost.

Looking, in the growing darkness, at this crowd of men and women, casually listening to music which made no solemn demand on the emotions, so like other each they could be sent to any other planet and form at once a French province, so unlike that no one in his senses would mistake them for a tribe, I was seized with rage to think that it was menaced by a nation which has re-invented torture, and squeezes a child's skull to make it like all the other skulls. They will crush this imperfect exquisite growth, plant of which the seeds have blown across Europe. Why ? Because they themselves grow nothing, they only, and with the ingenuity of insects, make ? I recalled a charming young German of good Bavarian family. He had been reading at Oxford about the English troops during the Peninsular War : Wellington trained them so strictly that when they entered France they astonished the peasants by paying for the cattle they took. He was scornful, and above all puzzled.

" Why, when you have fought and conquered, pay ? It doesn't make sense." Impossible to make him believe that there are other senses than those which flower impartially in music, coupling, and bombs.

And the Germany our grandfathers loved ? And the evenings of music, the sighs and linden-trees and candid welcoming voices ? Hard to believe they were the first victims of the German destined to rule. But what did we love, with — even while we ran to throw our arms round it — a touch of condescension and contempt ? A country we did not think of as a rival. And we gave it back, as a present, the innocence it offered us in the voices of children singing old carols. Flaubert could have told my grandfather — who never heard of him and would have detested him if he had — a little about *ces officiers qui cassent des glaces, en gants blancs, qui savent le sanscrit et qui se ruent sur le champagne, qui vous volent votre montre et vous envoient ensuite leur carte de visite, cette guerre pour de l'argent, ces civilisés sauvages.* . . . No. It has gone, that country we half loved and half invented, buried deeper than my Saloon. That, at least, had a true innocence, one I can feel in it when, fresh in its light air and the strong rough grass of its cliff, it rises from the past. There was a Saloon ; there was never a Germany, but only — until fifty years ago — a fair-ground of contradictory passions, for friendship, for innocent pleasure, for symphonies, for discipline, pillage, cruelty, learning, chasing each other to the music of an organ driven by one engine. And suddenly the music stops, and the children on the wooden horses become murderers.

Ah, Monsieur Bienvenu is bowing from the bandstand, and the Musique Municipale de Saumur is packing to go home — to another of these small towns where the past has not the slightest difficulty in making itself heard in any moment of the present, since they are cut out of the same cloth, endlessly unfolding, like the Loire at Saumur its pattern of vines, poplars, old strong roofs, like the habits handed down so carefully in a family that even before he can stand the youngest knows what is being said to him by everything he touches.

There is nothing to hope for unless this simplicity of the French spreads. Suppose each Englishman gave up his nagging

belief that he ought to live better and better and chose instead
to live well ? And the Germans gave up their form of ostenta-
tion — their macht-politik ? Need the French give up anything ? Yes. A few of them might perhaps learn English.

*

20 August. Why, when war is going to break out, don't
women hide their sons ? Or cry, all of them with the same
anger and pity : *No* ! It must be that each thinks she is alone,
that the others will not hear. Their sons, too, are alone.

And the little people in all countries, who left themselves
in the hands of men they trusted to look after them ? . . . We
cannot suddenly take back our freedom. Which of us even
knows what it looks like ? In a Lyons this morning a young
woman carrying her baby, a very handsome baby, said to my
sister,

"Look at him. I've never had a safe moment with him.
He was born in the May crisis of last year, and it's been the
same thing ever since." She added in a confident voice, "If
we'd had Anthony Eden this would never have happened."

What a charming illusion, smiling, elegant, on the eve of
a war !

*

"And you writers ? What have you to be proud of ? "
"Nothing," I said.

It is true. Survivors of the generation mutilated by the
other war, how have we used our twenty grace years ? Over
and above arguments, useless enough to be impudent, about the
relative vileness of air-raids and concentration camps, about our
duty to society and our right to be quietly ourselves, we forced
on a younger generation our despair and growing bitterness,
which were not of their size. We ought to have been affirming,
praising, a few simple things, those which underlie disillusion.
. . . We even proved that the brotherhood of the trenches had
been a snare — yes, at a moment when we should have been
repeating over and over again that a creed, any creed, which
sets loyalty to a party above the loyalty to each other of human
beings, condemns itself by that one simple unforgivable

treachery. Imbeciles, who did not see that now, now, when half the world is spanned by a bombing plane, it needs, to avert this new terror, a new outbreak of human loyalty, indivisible. . . . In the moment when this war, foreseen by so many of us and not even delayed by our cries, is here, and precipitates in our confused minds the certainty that fighting is better than submission, it is too late to look for a faith. We fall back on positions which have not been prepared. We see, when it is too late, our guilt. · I am as guilty of this war, I admit it, as the lazy or stiff and blind old men.

There will always be barbarians. Defeated by a supreme effort, they will always return. I know this habit of barbarians because I am one. . . .

When a friend who has always been right tells you not to hope, you hope because this may be his only chance of being wrong. I must hope. We are not at war yet. There is time. There are a few hours, a few days, weeks. No mother is being forced to deliver up her son tonight. It may not happen. Cowardly and obstinate, I give myself another night not to believe it, to believe in a miracle. If it is a clear fine night, there will be no war. . . . Not a cloud. . . . I am not frankly an egoist, I give this peaceful consoling night to all mothers and wives, and to the young whose first war this will be.

*

Someone in another house is playing tunes from the musical comedies of the last war. What an idea ! Why choose this evening to fill the stalls of an absent theatre with all those young men in uniform, younger than anything except their eyes, laughing, their hands and bodies restless with life ? It is only now that they are really disappearing, when a street will not suddenly remind us of them, and no book, carelessly opened, let fall one of their letters, no strangely bright day, no night over-full of stars, persuade us that they will come in and find us unchanged.

Nothing is left of that war — it is foolish to recall it — nothing of that long-drawn-out suspense and fever. And none of the excitement which, at least for the young, never quite failed until it was over. It was less excitement than the absence of real joy. And, too, the absence of real fear, the sort which creeps into the memory and inserts itself in every moment of the present. That waited to be born until after the war. . . . Of my brother, nothing is left but those few childish letters he wrote from France, between his seventeenth and nineteenth birthdays. Ought I to tear them up ? Tell me — what is the use of keeping things they touched, who have no hands now to touch anything ?

Only today I realise — it was as soon as her son was killed that my mother gave herself up entirely to her boredom, of which in the end she died. If she had taken the trouble, she would have lived to be old, like others of her family. But some even of those I remember died of boredom.

*

One lives during these days in a double, which moves its hands, walks about, argues. One's self is ashamed, and going about like a woman who has no right to be pregnant. (Perhaps that is why no one in my family, not a soul, has spoken to me about my son.) But it is really absurd to discuss whether we ought or ought not to attend a congress of writers in Stockholm next week. Everybody here knows that by next week we shall be at war. I suggest sending a wire to Paris to ask their opinion, and another to the Swedish writers. Everyone agrees — everyone, that is, except the only important person in the room. H. G. Wells insists — he is good-tempered and smiling, and obstinate — that we ought to go to Stockholm, to show that we are not afraid, to put heart into the French writers, who are all of them bureaucrats, and to speak, in a voice which will be heard by the whole world, for freedom. My belief is that the world is listening for some other sound, and I have no intention, whatever I may have promised a week ago, of being in Sweden when the war starts. These are the feelings of my real self, which is mute. The other says, and even snaps its fingers — how few times I was able as a child to make this defiant sound ; I practised it to a high degree of skill, secretly : the chances to use it now are so few that I daren't miss one — it is no use going to Sweden for the sake of a metaphor. Very well, he says amiably, he will go alone, and while the rest of us are cowering in England. . . . Is the war being fought in Sweden? my double says sharply: I could not have stopped her in time . . . he will be in Stockholm, warning the Swedish writers that we are cowards. Then he made one of the quips which are worth his arbitrary temper — at least in the moments when one is not suffering from it. The most mischievous of great men, and the least rigid, he has too quick a sense of humour to play at being great. This would be disconcerting, and humiliate his inferiors, if he had not also so many prejudices that they can pride themselves on being saner. It is an illusion.

"I shall be at Tilbury on Thursday," he said, "to sail on the *Suecia*."

We corrected him. "Wednesday."

Smiling, he began to turn the leaves of his diary. "It would be strange if I were saved by a subterfuge while the rest of you sailed to a concentration camp in Sweden. . . ."

Henry Nevinson was there. He had been silent. Suddenly he said, in his extinguished voice — the lava, under the weak tension of the surface, is still warm — that he had written to Rome protesting against one of the poems in a journal the Italian writers send us every month. A poem? About what? Oh — thanking the Duce for the joy of machine-gunning Abyssinians from the air, like black ants.

"What was the phrase?" Wells asked sharply.

"Like black ants," Nevinson repeated.

"Black . . . ? oh, yes, ants." He seemed to ponder the justice of the comparison. For a moment he looked exhausted, as though he had stared so long, and with no moral indignation to inflate him, into the endless mean corridors of tyranny, that he had nothing left to say. . . .

*

How strange it is that when war is really here — after the days on days of almost unbearable waiting, of listening to wireless orders about the children being sent out of danger areas, food hoarding, mobilisation, Poland invaded, Warsaw, Cracow,

Lodz bombed, the eloquence of politicians raising memorials to young men who are still alive and able to hear, an excited Frenchman on Radio Paris invoking the judgement of history, as if he knew in advance what history with her blind fingers feeling the marble will guess, of waiting for a letter which never comes, of waiting — it is not in the least strange. Exactly what happens? You turn on the wireless and hear a voice say smoothly, "Stand by for an important announcement." The announcement is short. We, he says, have given Germany until 11 A.M. to withdraw from Poland. At 11.15 the Prime Minister will speak — no, make a statement. That left an hour and a quarter. I finished the dusting and wrote a few sentences of Europe to Let : they were about Prague last year, but between my memories and the present moment the only channel was my mind which chose words, felt the weight of a sentence and lightened it by altering the form, turned to look at the river under the Karlðv bridge, it ran quickly and silently, and back to the page under my hand : no spark joined their hour to this : an agony starting in the past turned off before it could reach ours, and I felt nothing. During this time my body must have been attending to something else, because it stood up and went downstairs exactly in time to hear an old man's bitter voice say "Consequently we are at war with Germany."

It was a day of clear sun, the sky very bright, the wind high and soft.

The war had come quietly into the room. As he came in, we recognised him. He was a neighbour. There was nothing in his face to suggest death or the horror of the brains clinging to the bombed wall. He was no taller than any of us, and he gave his orders in a polite voice — fill sacks with earth from the garden to protect the windows of the cellars, carry there a table, chairs, and pack a suitcase with toys and rugs which could be snatched up when the raids started, make a list of the few stores we could buy. To other peoples he had come openly as a murderer : with us he observed certain forms. No one could have been more unassuming and willing to adapt himself to our simple life. I understood why we endure wars. It was only when he opened the door of the bathroom and stood there watching me as I tried to grasp the warm slippery bodies of the children, and when, looking in one of my mother's books, I noticed for the first time — what malice time shows — a few words she had written on the fly-leaf, in 1917, about my brother, that I felt fear. Oh, break all mirrors : in the world. Let us have no more reflected images ; let us rather be dumb to each other, and absent. Barren.

*

5 September. The past is able to close round certain moments, as if they were seeds, and deliver them again fresh and living in the present. But sometimes a present moment turns under our eyes into a remote past, and that is a death. It happened to me today to see these two reflected rays cross each other. Waiting for my local train to London, I saw a train filled with men in khaki, the first since the other war. They were the same, young in their clumsy uniforms, crowding with the same voices and gestures to the windows : I only had changed. Then I was tireless and confident, a young woman with her baby. Now, he is in the new war, and I, I am quickly tired, my body less supple, my mind cloudy and tortuous, without those horizonless hopes. So, I thought, the past ages so slowly that it will easily outlive me. . . . But who, at any moment, knows whether he is living in the past, or in how deeply buried a past ? A friend had invited me to dine with her at the Ivy : the room was crowded with people I knew, or their faces were familiar because I had seen them often before in this friendly restaurant. I noticed that there was not yet a uniform in the place. Suddenly I thought that something was happening in the room, and I looked up and caught all these people, known and unknown, in the very act of becoming nothing if not a memory. They had not changed in any way, none of them was more than a minute older, but during that minute they had become part of a past only distant enough to be old-fashioned and without, as yet, a meaning. Their faces indeed made no meaning — they were a syllable endlessly repeated, ba, ba, ba. Or the unrecognisable faces of drowned men. The silence would have alarmed me if I had not recognised it.

In the half darkness of the Circus, at the intersection of these two moments, two figures had been waiting. The first was the middle-aged prostitute wearing her professional fox fur over one shoulder and her gas-mask over the other. Near her, the old man offering, with a total indifference, a few laces : he had forgotten why he was standing there, so without hope that he had become the absence of himself, a vacant place in the street and the street was being sucked into it.

*

Obliviously where he stands
Nothing, nor the strings laid
Lax as dead Christ across the forgiving hands
Of the Marys across his, made

Light move in the dry fountain he became
When all his life fled into this palm,
Arctic upspringing sheaf, quick to claim
What silent No of alms ?

A pure light the lamps refute
Endlessly evokes this five-fold wick, cold
Source of flame, and mute
Trumpet of the rejoicing bone, void where rolled

By the same No abolished, and were lost
The glittering axles of the street, women's
Hands gripping their masks, default or flight of Eros
And the spiteful innocence

Of children from whose eyes the stones press
A young sun, suspense
In their sons of mothers that resembles breasts,
Cries breathing silence . . .

O heart of the rejected beating out absence
And the death of the world.

*

16 September. I have spent the day drafting a letter — to go to the centres of the P.E.N. in all allied and neutral countries. It has given me a great deal of trouble, and clearly is not all written from the same level. To say, " We, a democratic nation ", is not true on the same level as other things are true

— as that lies corrode the society which builds on them. But if there are an unknown number of steps leading down to what would be true if one could reach complete disinterest, there are also many people who will refuse to descend more than one of them. They must make what they can of my letter, which moves clumsily from step to step, not always down.

A war which, so little as I can judge, may last five years, will certainly poison us. There may come a time when I shall no longer understand how it can be possible not to hate. Or we may be invaded. For that reason, and one other, I am copying my letter — to confront it later with myself. The other reason is that many people would disapprove of this letter : if I am killed I should like this mild snap of my fingers to be left here.

With the outbreak of war, the value of the P.E.N. has increased a hundred-fold. Its responsibilities have increased in like measure. In what has come to be called totalitarian war the life of the spirit is as much threatened as the life of the body, and its death is the greater disaster. The natural instinct of officials and of what are called men of action is to suppose that such an activity as literature can easily, even usefully, be pushed aside in war. Or they will allow or even encourage writers to live as propagandists but not otherwise. This open neglect of literature and the other arts is only what can be endured and outlived. The worst is the danger in which war puts all we intend when we speak of civilisation. If the fearful urgencies of war are allowed to invade every part of life, not only our homes but our minds, and not only our minds but the Reason or Imagination, they will silence our belief that men, being all of them human or being all the children of God, ought to respect each other. It is not pleasant to imagine a future in which this belief has been destroyed.

Writers sometimes talk as though they were the only friends of civilisation. This is their conceit. But they have special powers to serve — or to corrupt — civilisation, and are obliged to use them. At this moment we see that the civilisation we know most intimately, having been brought up in it, is abominably in danger. If we should have a long war, we shall begin to hate whole nations, and to wish to punish them by every means in our power. We shall justify ourselves in using hideous means by the excuse that they shorten the war. Or the enemy nation will be the first to use such means and we shall retaliate. We, a democratic nation, have begun war with

I

the greatest reluctance, with no aim except to curb aggression. We see already, and shall see more clearly in a short time, the extreme difficulty of fighting a war without the help of an aggressive spirit in ourselves. If we are to be stiffened to a conclusive war, we shall learn to hate. If we suffer horrors we shall be tempted to return them, even though civilisation cannot survive another merciless slaughter. The irrationality we have deplored in Nazi Germany will take hold on us. In our effort as defenders of civilisation we shall end by cutting its throat.

It is a duty of writers to hinder in every way the growth of hatred and contempt for the enemy nation. A writer who persuades us to hate is ensuring that we are unfit to make peace. One of his tasks is to keep us sane ; to remind us that certain forms of warfare can be used only at the cost of destroying civilisation ; to stiffen us against the indecency, the blunders, of hate and revenge.

We, a democratic nation, have long been accustomed to think, speak, and write with a notable freedom. We pride ourselves on refusing to be led by the nose by our leaders. Probably we pride ourselves too easily. But undeniably there are among us enough stubborn individuals to give trouble to any over-eager authority. We are justified in speaking of our tradition of freedom. At war with a totalitarian state, we run a terrible risk of losing this freedom. One prohibition and regulation follows another to make us militarily efficient. Free speech, never much liked by authority, is discovered to be a danger. It is impossible to allow much freedom of action. All must be kept under observation, all must obey. People must be told what is expedient for them to know. They must write what can serve or at least cannot hinder the interests of a state at war. In this way our inherited right to discuss and enquire freely is easily taken from us. If we are not very careful, a freedom which has taken centuries to grow will in a few months be cut back by nervous or jealous authorities. No one has a closer interest in guarding this freedom than writers. We want to save the forms of civilisation as they exist for us in our fields, homes, and cities. But without the spirit the form would be worth less to us. It would be worth very little. Therefore we must not allow our minds to submit to any restraint that may be imposed by war on our bodies.

The writer spends his life trying to give a correct account of what he feels ; trying to penetrate the nature of reality ; trying to communicate the result of his experiments and exploration ; in short, trying to tell the truth. In peace time he is not often molested in his pursuit of truth, though he will be made clearly to understand that he is pleasing himself. Governments at war only care about truth if it is useful. The disinterested pursuit of truth in war time is at best useless ; at worst, a danger to the state. The old quarrel between truth and expediency is settled at once, in favour of expediency.

A state can support itself for a time by telling lies, but at the cost of corroding the very basis of civilisation, which rests — it can rest nowhere else — on the trust one man, one body of men, one country, can place in the others. When this is destroyed, the whole falls into rottenness. The first to suffer by the suppression of truth, writers ought to be ceaselessly and anxiously on the watch. If they are for-bidden to publish truth, they can remember, and wait their time. They can discourage lies, and what are worse, half-lies. Their plainest duty in war time is thus one they owe to their conscience and to society : they should be thankful that for once self-approval and the public service require the same difficult effort.

In the eighteen years of its existence the P.E.N. has been able to create innumerable strong ties between writers of all countries. The strength of these has been well tested during the strain of the past few years. We are to endure a severer test than any. We shall prove in ourselves that there exists a reality of intellectual and spiritual life which is in danger from invading armies only if we allow it to be. It can be defended by an act of will and faith. No other means exist to defend it. There is no vagueness about what we are required to defend or about our responsibility. We are required precisely to defend the integrity of the written word ; to think our own thoughts, not any provided for us ; to know beyond doubt that the only hope for the future rests on our being able to keep open as many channels as possible for the movement of ideas ; to repeat, if necessary to die repeating that any word, any act, any treaty, which debases the dignity and freedom of common men is evil and to be rejected.

The English P.E.N. salutes every other Centre. To the Centres in the neutral countries, we know how heavy your responsibility is and that you are equal to it.

I cannot help wondering how many of these sentences would sound if they could be heard by a man whose gaolers have been torturing him. But it is no use trying to live in an experience not our own.

*

This ear in my room — used to the delirium of Europe — is easily switched off. Its benefits are lies, trivialities, and a little Mozart ; if I were forced to attend to it for the whole of a day, I should go out of my mind. But nothing can shut off this invisible ear growing in me. It listens avidly to the murmur of voices coming through the cracks in my life, and is deaf only when I implore it to hear. During the news this evening, they broadcast the record, made in France, of an Irish regiment moving out along a road. Rain, mud, thin October poplars, and then the pipes playing an air the speaker called *Killelly*. But it was a song of my mother's ; she was in one of those rare moods when a young lively tomboy possessed her — and about *Killaloo. . . . You may talk of Bonaparty, Or any other party, And commong voo parley voo. . . . And two doctors from the South Took two days to find his mouth Which had somehow got concealed behind his ear. . . .* The pipes are only the lack of her voice, full, clear, itself a prisoner of this other ear which is mine and not obedient, deaf whenever it chooses, and when it chooses quick with voices. And, ah, cruel, before I can turn away, the room is full of other echoes. . . . *O fair dove ! O fond dove, Dove with the white white breast, Let me alone, the dream is my own, And my heart is full of rest. . . .* Towards the end, the dove *did mourn, and mourn, and mourn . . .* and my mother broke into her loud ringing laugh. Yet she never laughed over the just as absurd *Stay, steersman, Oh ! stay thy flight, Down the river of years. . . . Moor thy bark to the shelving glade, Where as children we laughed and played. . . . Stay ! Stay ! Stay ! . . .* Sadness rose with her voice and made us lightly uneasy. What tide, what shores, what great waves ? Half in terror of making a mistake, and half to avoid the sadness, I gave all my attention to the music ; my fingers would not stretch an octave, and I could reach the pedals only by slipping quickly on and off the stool. . . . I had forgotten it, words, tune, piano reflecting in its dark surface the sun sliding below the cliffs, the cry, startling me, of a gull, the weak mignonette scent ; it has the false clearness of what is remembered, fresher, livelier, than the room I am standing in, and all a lie.

*

Has not this verse from one of Barnes's poems the very sound of the blinds being drawn up and a window opened in the house ? O grief, that the absence of a mother must take its place among the other things in common use, and carelessly handled.

Vor daughters ha' mornen when mothers ha' night
An' there's beauty alive when the feäirest is dead ;
As when woone sparklèn weave do sink down from the light,
Another do come up an' catch it instead. . . .

Either let me come to you in your night, or come here and let us go back together to your noon and my morning.

*

1940

   28 January. Yesterday when I opened my bedroom windows at night — I must open them, though it means struggling with the black-out — I noticed the curious sound made in the trees by the light wind, a dulled chinking or creaking sound, like fragments of glass being moved . . . *rats' feet over broken glass in our dry cellar.* . . . I didn't understand it until this morning when I saw that some time after dark yesterday afternoon each blade of grass, twig, thin branch, had had drawn strongly over it a sheath of ice. The leaves of the privet and the sprays of evergreen firs were held, each separately, in its icy double, the grass had stiffened into transparent bodkins, a thin greenish-brown vein threaded them ; and the reeds ; in the growing light the bare branches and twigs of the apple-trees looked to be of glass, reflecting the tree. The ground had frozen under an inch-thick glacier, and the north wall of the house was a dull mirror. By noon, the wind had strengthened a little and the creaking sounds were louder. We took the children out to look at this superb but brittle world. Nicholas was amused but not startled. Why not a new world ? Judy, who is a year and eight months, looked at it from her blue eyes, clear mirrors of so much cold, and said nothing.

   29 January. During the night it snowed. Still fast in their ice, the leaves and branches now have a layer of snow. The electricity has failed, we got breakfast and ate it in the weak light of candles : the telephone wires, too, are down. When you step outside, the cold cuts the breath off in your throat. No sun, and the sky swollen with snow.

   30 January. Still the cold. And the whiteness of snow lying over the reflection in ice of leaves and branches. The big rhododendron gives itself the airs of a cactus, each leaf swollen to a monstrous thickness by the ice — a grey green-tinged icy flesh. If Europe were held a long time in this sterile flesh all the plants and seeds would die in it and the war end in famine. The light today smells of the frozen yews, veined by a dark sap.

31 January. This is the fourth day of the ice. The air is perfectly still. A vapour has been stretched out behind the trees, immobile now in the greyness. The tallest, a very old acacia, is split along all its branches, and many bushes have snapped off at the roots and frozen to the soil. The lawn is dazzling without light — spikes of ice, the once living grass, thrust out of the snow in a few places and where they are thickest look like miniature tank-traps. The children amuse themselves by running against bushes to start the sound of glass rods ringing together, surprisingly loud, and then branches snap off. . . . This evening I found, fallen to the back of a shelf, Valéry's *Variété 2*. I must have bought it in Bordeaux, the July before the war — but how did I come to forget it ? Perhaps by grace of some instinct warning me I should have more use of it later. When I cut the leaves I saw, with a shock of pleasure, that it had essays on Stendhal, Baudelaire, Mallarmé. Imagine it, in the trough of the war, to come on this island of calm energy and intense massive light.

*

5 February. The days are easy : there are beds to make, the children, stoves, a novel about Alsace which I must finish. I have never in my life been able to feel that it did not matter when I finished a book. I write slowly, very slowly, and then, after the first few chapters, a nagging anxiety has inserted itself behind the others and presses on me with a growing force, until I am writing all day, to evening, scarcely able to bear the weight, and longing to be rid of it. Is it boredom ? Or a fear I have not named yet ? I can never understand how it is that other writers have so much time. They travel and do not take a manuscript with them, they live social lives and have love-affairs or quarrel with each other, or they run about making speeches. When do they read ? Or learn ? Or is it only my stupidity makes writing a trouble ?

It is at night I become a coward — when I put the light out and draw my curtains, and there is nothing for it but to lie down and remember the war. Then it is as if the air became water, my lungs struggle with it, trying to force it through my body, which can only lie there as though it must break open and let out this despair, and the agony of wanting the war to stop, now, quickly, to free us from the bad dreams. But it is real — the misery of poor women lying awake worrying about the rent and the future ; the children running loose in the cities without schools ; the anger of young men whose lives, at best, are being mutilated ; the drowning men, the men who at this moment, as I breathe this cold air, are being choked. " We all have to die." Yes, yes, but that is not the point. The point is my brother's unformed writing, of a child, and his awkward hands, and the little he had learned even of the simplest joys before his death was forced brutally into him.

*

None of my tricks — as an acrobat — has become second nature : I am still as slow and awkward as when I began. Today at a luncheon chiefly of writers, I found myself between the English novelist I respect more than any other and a young French diplomat. The novelist's charming gestures, feminine in their lightness, wrote a sentence of which in spite of my fear I was able to spell out a few syllables — a little and feline cruelty, goodness, honesty, care for justice. I had been prepared, by one of his countrymen, for the French diplomat — " He has spent years trying to look like Proust, but I think he has given it up as a bad job." As he came in I recognised him from this description and greeted him by name. Very slight, elegant, he moved with a languor which certainly had become natural, and he had not had to practise the air of indifference given him by eyelids drawn far down over coldly light eyes. I felt that I was seated beside a boredom so polished and insolent that mine, which I can never bring forward to help me at these moments, is only the anguish of a barbarian before the symbols of a culture he does not understand. It was fortunate for me that he chose to speak.

" How did you know me ? Do I look so like a diplomat ? "

I seized my courage to answer him. " Monsieur Y. said to me : If you see someone coming in who looks as though Proust might have written about him, that is Monsieur de X."

" That is a compliment," he said, without a smile. He was none the less pleased, and in answer to a confused remark of mine about the fatuity of asking writers to eat in public in honour of whatever person or event we were honouring, he roused himself to speak with a very faint tinge of interest, and at such length that I was able to attend without feeling anxious : he must, I thought, have decided to make a pretence of enjoying himself.

" My complaint about the English intellectuals " — in spite of its politeness, his voice gave away his complete disbelief in their existence — " is that they are not serious enough. For example, Mr. Wells, who is conducting a debate in one of your newspapers on the Rights of Man. Why doesn't he write about what is happening to these Rights in Poland ? The information we have is so frightful that little of it can be printed. The Germans, you know, are systematically shooting the edu- cated men and women, doctors, scientists, writers, professors ; they intend to make Poland a country of peasants and workers, uneducated men without leaders. Oh, you are going to say that these classes will throw up leaders among themselves. But history, you know, is the proof that they don't. . . . When I said that they are shooting the educated women I was sparing your feelings. And they have emptied whole towns and villages of their Polish inhabitants — simply turned them out to die in forty degrees of frost. They bring in a Baltic German, show him round the house, ask him if he likes it, then tell the Polish owner he has two hours to clear out. . . . This is not your house any longer, it belongs to this man. — Where am I to go ? — That is not our business. — What can I take ? — What you can carry in your hand. . . . There is no other house for him and his family to go to ; they join the thousands who are dying on the frozen roads." He lifted a hand, smaller and a great deal smoother than mine, and looked at it with an interest which destroyed a little the effect of his words. He was sincere, but he would have been more immediately moved if he had suddenly developed a chilblain. In a tone of ironical satisfaction, he went on, " Just seventy years ago, Flaubert wrote to a novelist, a woman : *A qui donc sert la science, puisque ce peuple, plein de savants, commet des abominations dignes des Huns et pire que les leurs, car elle sont systématiques, froides, voulues, et n'ont pour excuse ni la passion ni la faim ?* . . . I don't admire Flaubert, he is a master of the devastatingly flat epithet, but he understood the Germans, and his sentence is equally just today."

The severe contrast between his voice, cultivated to the point of being almost inaudible, too exhausted to bear any emotion, and the scenes of vile cruelty it called up, made them more shocking than any excited story would have been. It was as though the delicate hand he was resting on the table had opened to display an obscene instrument of torture. I felt myself trembling. But it was partly nerves, and since I must not completely disgrace myself — I was already, I felt, disgraced by my lack of wit — I said hurriedly, " But we still have to decide what to do with the Germans ; they have so much energy, it drives them again and again to destroy the world and replace it by a hideously enlarged model of Germany — *amoureuse de la mort et des extrêmes.* We can't hold them down by force. We can do it for a time, then people become bored."

" I know," he said coldly.

" The English become bored first."

He smiled. " I'm sure you haven't read the Yellow Book just published ? English writers are not interested in foreign affairs. I'm speaking, you know, about the reports of our Ambassador to Berlin."

But I had read it. My anxious wish to please drove me to say — it was a polite exaggeration, but not a lie — " The penetration your Ambassador showed in his reports, and their clarity, are a little humiliating, placed beside our own reports from Berlin. Perhaps if we had educated ours at the École des Sciences Politiques . . ."

" But everyone knows that your Ambassador to Berlin is a fool. They are not all like him."

He had spoken without a trace of irony, as though it would

be paying a nobody too much honour to despise him. I felt an impulse to destroy this calm. " One hears disquieting things from France. Is it true that some Frenchmen, or a class, are more afraid of socialism than of Hitler ? "

He shrugged his shoulders. " The real struggle in this war will be across the body of my country, between England and Germany. Both are capable of a terrible force, the Germans from greed, the English because they have been wounded in their pride ; some people would call it vanity. They may destroy themselves in their rage. That is, if Germany begins the attack."

" And France ? " I asked.

For the first time I saw, stretched lightly under the air of disdain and boredom with which he had contrived his, as it were, Proustian face, another which may not have been any more natural to him but was at least unfinished — it was still capable of change ; it had a touch even of real bitterness, like the suspicion of garlic in an honest salad.

" If we must become a dependency of the British Empire, let us do it with a good grace," he said. . . .

I don't understand the France I heard, or I thought I heard, speaking in his voice — deliberately fatigued. Are they tired already ? I won't think about it. Think instead of any village in the Dordogne, at midday in summer — empty, because of the heat, and silent, with a silence which vibrates when you lay your hand on an old house. No country is less likely to disappear than this one where the silence has the taste of a young wine.

*

26 April. He is so intelligent that I never understood why he thinks it worth while talking to me. I am nervous with him, but I have begun, in spite of myself, to form an idea of him which is not simply a polite reflection. The youngest of four brothers, if he had allowed a family habit to choose for him he would have been a soldier, a scholar, or a civil servant ; he is not able, speaking five languages, and with friends or at worst colleagues in a dozen countries, to speak with conviction more than one, his own. He is very fond of his brothers, but he thinks the professor of mediaeval German half an alien, and the Treasury official a bit of a grocer in his attitude to money ; he is completely at his ease only with his eldest brother, Aden, the general. Aden shares his liking — the nearest thing in his life to a passion — for Horace Walpole. Walpole has sat with him through international monetary conferences, and it is Walpole's philosophy, without illusions about human beings, cool, self-centred, with a warm spring of feminine kindness, which gives my friend his reputation for imperturbable honesty and vanity. His colleagues, in every country, respect him ; but because he never loses his temper, and drinks claret, the director in Berlin considered him francophile and a gourmand ; and in Paris, since the day when a private letter was handed about in which he remarked on the trouble taken by the greatest French writers to turn charming platitudes, he is said to be a socialist. In fact he is purely and arrogantly English. He distrusts in the French their habit of logical thought, whereby words weigh the same on every occasion, without any allowance for their evaporation in anger or solidifying in a moment of danger, and in the Germans he dislikes their trick of loading a word with myths — so that to say mountain is to say exultance, the superman, vengeance, or any other madness proper to a legend — and above all that primitive mysticism always waiting its chance to throw them into an ecstasy where each German identifies himself with all the others and yearns to consummate the marriage of the German tribe with the planet. Even in looks he is the Englishman of foreign cartoons, excessively tall, thin, and long-nosed. All this masks neatly a mind which never allows a feeling to disguise itself as a reason, or an idea to show him only one of its faces. He has a right to his unconscious vanity.

What moved him today to explain to me, after he had read out sentences from his brother's letter, the frightful seriousness of our position ? He explained it very fully, in his quiet voice, even smiling a little. It seems that never, never at any time during the last war, were we in such mortal danger as we are now. We have not been threatened in this way since the Napoleonic wars. *We may lose this war.* Compared with the Germans, we are very poorly equipped, and the French, etc. etc.

I am tired of being told that the French are suffering a crisis of prudence and logic. (His brother distrusts them for a quite different reason. What can you expect of a nation in which sentinel is a feminine noun?) He talked for almost an hour, as though it were important to destroy the illusions of an obscure writer. Why? I think, from curiosity, and a sprig of malice, to see how I would take it. Little he knows me. I knew that my face was dull, even vacant. It was perhaps that provoked him into going on, as once years ago it provoked a surgeon to tell me the truth about an operation. In fact, behind my air of stupidity, I was listening as I would to angrily loud voices heard at night in a foreign town, trying on them one meaning after another to find the one which does not imply a murder. What meaning has the word defeat for us? We have never seen an execution.

" My dear child," he said, " what really frightens me is the appalling indecision of these old men! They have committed us to a war they're not fit in any way to run. I think — I hope — they'll be sacked. We're very generous and sentimental, we're always ready if a man confesses his fatal mistake to praise him for committing it. But these aged sinners are not going to repent. . . . You know I never liked Churchill " — he had a rooted distaste for Mr. Churchill's prose, so unlike Horace Walpole's — " but I tell you we need his pugnacity and his impulse to rule — these lawyers and business men don't rule: they manage, and meanly enough. He would give the country a personal faith . . . which might last the war. After that . . ."

I asked him about Norway, and again, stooping over the map in *The Times*, he showed me that things are going wrong there — in spite of the reports. He told me which names to listen for on the wireless and what it will imply if we are said to be retiring, whatever reason is given, from certain places.

Finally, and as if he really were disappointed by my dullness, he said gently, " Do you understand what I've been saying? "

" Oh, I think so," I said. " You are telling me that we may be conquered. And the German meaning of the word, I know, is cruelty, hunger, fear. Or our old gentlemen may capitulate, which is the same thing. Or then perhaps there would be an interval when people young enough to stand it could reach America."

"I thought I should have to convince you." His smile covers so much vanity and kindness. Why did he not guess that I might be hiding from him — out of shame — my lack of logic? I find it impossible to believe in our defeat. I'll keep my eyes open, I'll watch. *But I do not believe it.* Let them go on quarrelling with me in my nerves — the one who says: That is only because defeat is not English — and the other: Suppose we are defeated? What will happen to your son? . . . My disbelief is stupidity or stubbornness or belief.

*

2 May. It was foolish to accept, for this afternoon, an invitation from my Norwegian friends. But if I had made an excuse, next time I went they would have said — with that northern malice I recognise — " So you had to retreat last week, too ? "

To be honest, I was not sure when the news would be let out. I thought I should be lucky. But while I was there the telephone rang, from the Legation, and my friend answered it ; I watched the changes on her face. She looked at the others in the room — all Norwegians — and at me, and choosing with superb politeness among her pronouns,

" We are leaving Norway," she said.

I had to sit there and listen to the Norwegians talking among themselves. They dropped at once their half-sarcastic, half-candid friendliness, but — out of courtesy or to punish me — they spoke English, leaving in their own language the bitterness they felt and the memories pressing their terrible weight on each word. After a time I did not listen. I had my own sorrow, different but sharp.

It is as if Europe were evaporating, leaving a discoloured mark in the flask. . . . When I went to Norway I landed at Horten, at four o'clock in the morning. This small port moved me like a memory. A name common in our family was written on a door in the street nearest the harbour. It had made a quicker crossing — no, it had always been here, refusing exile and to lose the perennial cool vigour of this north. The streets sleeping in the clear light were familiar although I had not seen them before. They had the narrow simplicity of streets I knew as a child and from a memory older than my own. The air was deliciously light and cool ; there was a faint smell of tar and new rope. I was sleepy, but it was exhilarating to be awake in this sunlight which sprang back from the modest houses and the small boats, in the instant it touched them. . . .

All that was five years ago. It is less than a month since the Germans bombed Horten, and destroyed — what have they destroyed ? — no, what have they left of this little town ? They are nearly unbearable, the extremes we have to hold together in our minds, with the insanity of a continent springing up to force them apart : the cool sunlight on the harbour and narrow streets with the bombs, the green icy stream in the high dale with the concentration camp. All that vileness and cruelty spreading its stain in the clear air. . . .

One of the Norwegians spoke directly to me — either his politeness or his anger had got the better of him.

" We knew quite well that if we resisted it meant that Norway would be a battlefield. All right, we said, we put it at your disposal as a battlefield ; if you can fight the Germans here you will never be invaded yourselves. . . . All ours, we said, will fight. . . . If you had landed sufficient forces in time, and gone straight for Trondheim, risking your ships, you would have pushed the Germans out."

" You will not now be a battlefield," I said foolishly.

" No — a concentration camp. . . . If every town in Norway had been destroyed and the Germans thrown out, we could still have been happy. . . . Scandinavia is gone, Sweden will be forced to make terms, the Balkan countries will see that they must capitulate quickly——"

He obeyed a glance from one of the others and stopped short. . . .

We lived during that summer on the island of Tjømø in the Oslo fjord. There was a small wharf, the wooden hotel, shabby and friendly, a few houses, a white dusty road running between pines and the fields in which sprang fantastic rocks, grey table-lands split open by ling and young trees. It was a rocky shore, and the water, clearer than any I have seen, was too deep except for swimmers. The wide fjord had all the sea light, the candour, missing from the dourly handsome fjords of the other coast. In the hot sun, the scent, like wild raspberries, of the pines, went to your head. It might alone have accounted for the vigour with which Norwegians, young men, and girls with the pallor of the north under their tan, danced, sang, and argued through the long evenings and the short scarcely dark nights until daylight. Their vigour is as inexhaustible and unexhausted as the cold rivers, alive with salmon, in the hills. In the late afternoon, a small steamer called at the island and it was not only the children who ran to the wharf to watch her make in. . . . I was writing, more quickly than I have ever written anything in my life, a novel about the second year of a dictatorship — I tried to explain in it why a dictator must murder the friends who were useful to him when he was only a brutal adventurer. It was laid in England, but during those weeks, writing as I did, all day, in the window of my wooden cell, my memory was drawing through suspense and treachery the clear Norwegian threads, scent of pines and salt, brushing of the long grass in the field, the pure sky without clouds, creak of dry sun-bleached wood. . . . Let it undo its work, then. Let it draw them out, as a nerve is drawn out until it snaps, and leave in place of the island a pure grief and cruelty . . . without benefit of that air. . . .

" I wasn't anxious about my father and mother — they were openly anti-Nazis — because although they lived in Oslo they had a hut in Hallendal — do you know it ? — and got away there. But this means that the country will be taken over by the Gestapo and they'll be caught." He laughed nervously. . . .

Oslo, when you look down on it at night, from the tall hill behind, is a small half-hoop of lights at the edge of the water. In the daytime it is the most charming capital in Europe, simple in its dignity of king's palace, university, harbour, so small the stranger has the illusion that he lived here at some time when he was happy. . . .

Chamberlain on the wireless — a very shrewd speech. The impression floating above his words, like a bird trying to insert itself into its shadow, was that we had been very clever to go to Norway in order to be able to withdraw so cleverly. Suddenly — it was nothing he had said, it emerged from the gap between his words and their meaning — my mind felt the approach through this invisible gap of a new threat.

" Is it possible," I said timidly, " that there is some other reason for withdrawing ? Is it possible that France is not such a powerful ally as we think ? "

They looked at me with a quick irony, and my friend said, gently enough, that if it were not for the French army there would be nothing for the continent to hope. " And think of our having to depend on the French ! " one of them cried. As if dependence on a Latin race were the last insult to a nation descended from Viking pirates.

*

They had come to this room from Europe, most of them after enormous difficulties which had changed and multiplied under their hands, as in those bad dreams when you pull frantically at the bolts of doors to escape a torturer. Others, although they had left in good time, were so poor when they got here that you really can't imagine how they live at all. Most of them are Germans and Austrians — people with whose country we are at war ; many but not all Jews, people with whom half of Europe has been at war for years : there are also a few Czechs ; and two, or three, Catalans, men with haggard delicate features, who have an air of being alone in the room. Each brings with him into the lighted room an immensely elongated shadow, a part of the blackness of Europe : caught up in it, fragments of the deaths and agonies they have escaped, faces, of people about whom they no longer know anything, are they dead or living, and how living ? died how ?, images of streets and rooms once so familiar they hardly saw them and now see with such clearness that one of them will stand in the London street and force open his eyes . . . because here there should have been a flight of steps and across the street a hand waved in greeting from the tables of a café . . . they come into this room, having dressed themselves with great care, a few have come only because we invited them, others with a crazy sense of relief — We do still exist, then ? Yes, yes, we must ; since who, if we were nothing, would invite us ? — others are thinking the whole time of their insecurity, so that when you look at their eyes the image given back is of pure desolation. They stand about in this over-lit room in their own dark.

There are not a great many of them — how many ? a hundred ? They could be changed into terms of the very many hundreds of letters written in answer to theirs coming to us from Vienna, Prague, Brno. . . . Their letters ? So many hands thrust from the earth which is being trodden over the mouth and eyes. Yes, but how many ? If at any time I knew, I have forgotten — a few, and only those we were able to save, or some of them saved themselves. I remember what I had better forget. The young Czech who wrote in frantic English from Brno, promising — to put himself in a good light with us — to " work desprite and when in war I fight " : his letters ceased before we were able to do anything. I remember the German writer from Prague whose wife had not followed him at once ; she was still in Prague when the Germans came : worn out by days of running from place to place imploring help he began when he was talking to me in the P.E.N. office to cry ; he did not know he was crying and looked with astonishment at the drops falling on his hands.

So few — but the effort to help is so much too large for us that we are almost broken, and all the help we give each of them is pitiably small, although with fearful trouble we begged about three thousand pounds. Does that seem to you a large amount of money or only a little ? For what it has to do, it is a very little. I would rather break stones than write any more begging letters.

And now the internments. . . .

The worst this evening is that I shall be forced to make a speech. At any time to have to speak drives me almost out of my mind with panic. But to have to address myself to this anxiety, this fear, even when hidden, of a personal defeat . . . people whose real lives have been torn from them so cruelly that they are as if flayed. . . .

The moment came when I had to stand on a chair and say what I had prepared. I only remember parts of it. . . . We English, I said, must bear our share of responsibility for the course of events in Europe. We have made many mistakes. We don't wish to make light of them. With all we did we did not manage to save Europe from war. And we are now at war. But we remember that the difficulties each of us is facing in his own life are lighter than yours. It is not easy to live as the stranger within the gates. We know that. We are sorry. If we could make it easier for you we would. We do anything we can and it is very little. We cannot give you back your homes, your familiar streets, your lost certainties. In the end, nothing is any good to you but your own courage, which we know to be great. It is on that you rely. . . . We are sharply conscious that our friendship is a plank thrown hurriedly across the uncertainty and coldness of your lives in this country. You must forgive us for that. You must also forgive us if our own new anxieties, and the confusion of the war, preoccupy us. You will not make the mistake of thinking that we are no longer concerned for you because we are concerned about ourselves. . . . In England, as in every country, there are people always ready to look with suspicion on the stranger. When these people accuse you, remember that they are our enemies as much as yours . . . enemies of all the P.E.N. believes — that justice is possible and that men must come one day to understanding their need of each other. As against them we are your allies. Do not forget this. Do not be betrayed into a dangerous anger and impatience. . . . For a few hours this evening we are all safe and all at our ease. I know you cannot forget the past, its pressure on you drove you here. But expect a future which will ask you for the whole of your energy and wits and give you in return a country. . . .

As soon as I had said this and jumped off my chair, I thought: But which of them is not so sunk in the past, so fastened to it by all the roots he was made to drag from their earth, that he has become it? That he goes on writing and re-writing between every line of his past, and in all the margins, until not an inch of space is left for the future to squeeze in one word? And this fire of twigs we light for them — what use is it except to make their cold darker ?

*

11 May. We were often in Antwerp when I was a child. As everything we remember of our childhood is more than itself, is the glance back and forward over a vast country, so Antwerp is the reflection, gently precise, in my mind, of its two least precise habits, eternity and what is foreign. They are perhaps the same image, reflected from two angles. I can trace the second as it fits itself into the outline of yellow shuttered houses, of a long room with many lace curtains and a parrot, of the dark cathedral and the flower-women in sunlight, of the shops we looked in so often and thoroughly that I noticed at once the slight, the very slight, changes made from week to week in their usual display . . . what a word for so firm a modesty ! . . . But its essence is in the dry husks we found spilled over the wharf when the ship docked there one June. What were they ? They were like the husks of some large seed which had dropped out to make room for this mysterious emptiness. Uncertain, and afraid of being laughed at if I asked, I stood beside my father and the agent and touched them lightly with my foot : foreign-ness came from them, a perfume I shall never smell, it was all strange scents and none of them, and which has enticed me ever since.

And the voyage to Antwerp — not the sea-crossing, which bored me on a steamer the size of a modern Channel ferry. I was the only passenger in the half-dozen berths leading off the saloon — my mother slept in my father's cabin on the bridge, next the chart-room — nothing to do, it never occurred to my mother, who was bored by the sea, that idleness bored her child, no books except the scrap book in which my father had copied jokes and poetry and sketched ladies in petticoats, bloomers, or corsets. No, not the sea-voyage, but the endless hours it took to move up the river to Antwerp, the thin line not horizon, widening slowly, how slowly, into flat green fields, a house, a Noah's-ark tree. Space, which at sea had shrunk to a few yards of deck, the tarred canvas of hatches, the saloon filled by its dining-table and fixed chairs, widened timelessly as the land came gently back into it ; there seemed no reason why it should cease, and the light shock with which finally we ran against the continent would have been a disappointment if it had not opened at once into the foreign town.

My dear Scheldt — image of eternity ; my dear Place Verte, my dear wharf and streets and music played at night in the Zoo, and eclairs at the counter of a small shop, and windows filled with padded brassières and lace — image of a pure joy : today the Germans bombed you, I don't know how badly. Little by little, destroying an eternity here, a child's toy there, they are emptying the world of seeds and words, leaving, this time, a husk filled only with loss.

*

It is only now, when our army is back in Belgium, that I feel the acute ceaseless anxiety, the anguish, I did not feel during 1914–18, when it was my own friends, the young men of my age, who were there. Twenty-five years after they were killed, I begin to be afraid for them in the living bodies of boys I don't know. In those days, the death of a young man shocked and grieved when it happened, and for a short time. But I was ambitious ; I hoped ; I believed in a future. Now I know that the world is poorer for every young man killed in battle and every child murdered by a bomb, and that the debt will have to be paid. It seems to me that my friends, those young men, with their illusions, gaiety, desires, faults, hopes, are now really dying in the deaths of another generation. And I have even heard these new ones say of ours that they were romantic about war and went blindly . . . to Loos and Passchendaele. . . .

It is their illusion. Every generation puts out its own, and when they begin seeding they resemble each other so closely that the earth, for all its experience, can't tell the difference.

*

When the Germans entered Prague, they chose a certain house as the place where the Gestapo would examine political prisoners. Innocent until then of all but human vices and crimes, an adultery or two, a child whipped unfairly, a few frauds or lies, it was forced to hide now — as well as these things can be hidden — an inhuman cruelty. There will be nothing for it, when Czechoslovakia is free, but to pull it down. Who would dare live with those walls ?

Among the thousands put to death in one of its rooms, after he had been tortured, was the man who in June 1938 was Minister of Education. That month he had the idea of giving, for the benefit of a writers' congress, a performance in Czech of Romeo and Juliet, in the garden room of the seventeenth-century palace which housed the Ministry. Open to the garden, its absent fourth wall was a triple arch, with white strong columns, a balustrade, and a shallow flight of steps. The play began at dusk, and the audience watched from the garden the dancers move up the steps into the panelled room, and through into the darkness, and the young men argue, quarrel, make love, with a boldly new vigour, as if translation into Czech had given Shakespeare the age of the Republic — twenty years. The sky was the colour of plums, young, hard, a little green on the side which caught only the last of the sun. . . . Suddenly, during a brief pause, Henry Nevinson glanced at it, and at the swallows, and the lucid summer dusk, the colour of silence, and said, " To think that all this will go on and in a few years I shan't be alive to see it ! " He should have said, " To think that in a few months the man who thought it well to play Romeo and Juliet in seventeenth-century Prague will be dying in the hands of his torturers." He should have said, " To think that in a few weeks his country will be crying to its allies — " Mercutio at this moment cried it — also in Czech — " *I was hurt under your arm.*" He should have said . . . but the young Shakespeare, stepping from behind a pillar, silenced him with a finger on his smiling mouth, and the young Republic, disdainful of treachery, not even hesitating to imagine a hundred possible futures, none of them of defeat, sprang in front of the steps and threw words against the unseen audience without dreaming a night, close enough, of fear, equally of words and silence.

*

20 May. The speed of the German advance is stupefying.

A triumphal march of tanks on day after day of unbroken sun-light, driving before it hordes of refugees. They are a pestilence, not an army. In a few days they will reach the coast. And then ? . . . We are anxious about the children, so near London and the south coast. I have written to A. in North Wales and N. in Scotland, to ask whether, if it became necessary, I could send my young sister and her children. . . . Meantime, I am trying to finish Cousin Honoré : if we are defeated I shall wish I had spent these last days looking at things, but it is no use setting one's watch by a time which may not be exact. The thought of the fighting in northern France is a deafness shutting off any fear except for the children.

Was there ever so young and fresh a May, the sky cloudless and the air purely clear and warm ? The acacias are fountains of ivory blossom, with a light scent which comes and goes, as the trees breathe. Or a fine smile ?

*

21 May. London. The choir of flowers in St. James's Park — singing ? no, shouting — heaven knows what, but it was certainly English. The paper I had bought said that the Germans have taken Amiens, Arras, Abbeville. All the names of the last war are rising to the surface, with all that was buried with them, the hands of young men, the fever, the joys, the shame. Standing looking into the lake, I saw the tanks lurch through the shabby square at Abbeville in the early sunlight, and an officer walk quickly into the narrow yard of the Tête de Bœuf, sit down resting his arm on the checked tablecloth and ask for coffee, rolls, honey. An absurd hallucination, as clear as the pain it started. Or am I beginning to mix dream and memory, like the skeins of two silks ?

I left the Park and walked and walked. The heat rising from the pavement crossed a column of sunlight at the height of my eyes. I was blind for a moment. Then, thankfully, I found I had reached the Chinese Embassy ; I had thought it farther away. Rooms, a staircase, receiving with indifference, polite, the chattering anxiety of English people mainly of the Left — since it is the Left, the side sensitive to a danger to life, which has been anxious about China during these years. Here and there in the voracious current a reed, a Chinese woman, her face clear, unaltered by its smile. There were small sandwiches, ambrosial enough, and strawberries and cream. . . . I listened with all my ears. . . . The French Ninth Army has been captured, and with it a General Giraud, who seems important, if any general in France is important now. . . . An editor who has been attacked many times in the Nazi press told me he had begun to carry poison to save himself and his wife from the Gestapo. . . . The platitudes oozing from a writer who will certainly, for the excellent reasons he will find, make friends with the Germans — if they conquer us. . . . A woman whose simplicity and elegance have always intimidated me talked to me about her children — she is a Jew. Tears came into her eyes without falling — " I would give them to friends now if I thought they could lose their identity and have a chance, only a chance, of living." Not knowing what to say, I was moved, as though she were dying and I was alone with her, to kiss her : it had been the right thing ; for a second she clung to my hands. . . . All these people assumed that the French are going to capitulate ; in a few days the Germans will take Paris and the coast facing England ; ill-equipped, led by generals of the last war, the French are demoralised, retreating from the tanks on to villages already burned by parachute troops. For once, her rivers have not saved France. They must have relied too nearly on the Marne, it has failed them and they are lost — as if all the rest, towns, cities, Paris, châteaux, vineyards, the Beauce, the Dordogne, the harbours, were held together by this one clasp : which has given way. . . . Even the Chinese Ambassador seems to expect that the French will give in. This impressed me more than anything I heard. More than the talk, reasonable enough, about England being devastated from the air and German armies landed here by troop-carrying planes. — " When ? " I asked the editor. — " Very quickly, I imagine. Within the next two months." — " And then ? " — " The Government will be forced to capitulate. . . ." — " And then ? " — " It depends on . . . provided that . . ." The mood of all these people was rigidly subjunctive.

I was dejected by the certainty, it seems of them all, that this is the end. In my heart, I did not entirely believe it. Neither, I suppose, did they — entirely. . . . The calm of the Chinese, and their smiles, friendly, indifferent, were self-effacing — as if they left the space free for their English guests to talk themselves out. . . .

The most terrible thing, the thing for which is no comfort, is the situation of our army, caught — if the Germans have reached the coast — in a triangle of country with no choice between massacre or surrender. Couldn't they, I asked X., try to fight their way out ? " My dear girl," he said drily, " three hundred thousand of them at the most, and the Germans have eight million men under arms. . . ."

I had to leave this desert of logic for one far worse — the dinner at which I had promised to speak. Imagine spending one of your few last evenings on this hideous custom of public dinners ! I made a vow. Deliver us from the invasion, and I will never, never, let myself be bullied into another. The hotel was full of Dutch refugees : we walked through rooms I thought were being spring-cleaned to a vast room covered with mirrors which repeated everything, like a chorus of idiots. I was doubly unhappy because I had been trying all day to telephone to my child at the aerodrome. X.'s wife had promised me to go on ringing up until she got him. She would tell him to come to their flat where I am staying, and I imagined him already there. The dinner, bad and ill-served, went on slowly. I grew desperate. My politeness failed and I asked if I might speak first, before the great man. As soon as I had spoken I left and took a cab to the X.s' flat. Before I could ask, they told me he was on his way in. He arrived at once. He looked so young, almost a child, that I felt an impulse to lie to him — the French are re-forming on the Seine, America has sent us a hundred thousand aeroplanes, fifty battleships, a battalion, plague has broken out in the German armies — I told him bluntly as much as I knew and we debated the possibility of defeat and what chance there was of our own aeroplanes being sent to Canada with their crews. " Thank goodness," I said, " you and I have different names now." He smiled quickly. " The Germans are not so

stupid as that. . . ." X. came in with one of the Chinese from
the Embassy, and again the talk was of France and defeat.
" Can't you get your mother away in an aeroplane ? " X. said :
" she's too well known as an anti-Nazi." " He has just married
a wife," I said quickly. " When the Germans come," X. said,
" you must get them both away." He smiled. X. and the
Chinese diplomat questioned him. Could the Fleet defend itself
against bombing ? Was it possible for the Americans to fly
their air fleet here ? etc. etc. At his age I was either too afraid
or too anxious to be approved of to speak. He answered very
well. He has matured in the last half-year. He was always,
even as a child, composed and able to speak sensibly, without
affectation or naïveté, but he has a young authority now, speaks
when he knows and only what he knows, quietly, with great
clearness.

It was two o'clock when I went to bed. I was exhausted,
but for a long time could not sleep. I thought of my unfinished
work, of my young sister and the children, of my son.

*

22 May. For three hours this afternoon I tried to advise and
comfort the wife of an Austrian writer, swept into internment
last week. Some of her English friends have refused to see her.
She is living alone in their cottage, and may herself be interned.
I wrote down everything about both of them, to do what I
could. She said she was afraid that when the Germans invade,
the refugees will be handed over to them. This shocked me.
Then I reflected that in the disorder they might be forgotten —
and found by their Nazi countrymen. . . . At the Ministry I
was told that Churchill has flown to Paris again to stiffen the
French. . . . I was hoping, although a second evening would
be a supreme piece of luck, to see my son again. In the evening
I rang the number he had given me. The man who answered
said, " They were late leaving." For a second I didn't understand, then realised he was telling me that the orders had come
and they were gone. No use to stay a second night with
X. I caught a late train. . . . The sky had kept a clear light—
an illusion — in the unlighted carriage it was too dark to read.

In this curiously still sky the balloons were black and shrunken, like squeezed grape-skins. An immense moon, so bright that it reflected a gleam or two of the sunset, rose on the left. The Thames was a glass, a real glass, the reflections in it of the trees clear and very sharp.

My sister had gone to bed. Usually she sleeps when her head touches the pillow — she must have been anxious ; when she heard us she came down. Her hair tumbled on her shoulders, she was a girl, younger than her years. My brother-in-law was still at the factory, which is on a twenty-four-hour shift, all our supplies in France have been lost. " Perhaps you and the children had better go to North Wales," I said. She shook her head, looking past me with our mother's stubbornness. " I can't leave all our fruit in the garden, it must be picked and bottled. We shall need it." It seemed a good reason, as good as mine for going on with Cousin Honoré.

24 May. The Germans have been in possession of Boulogne since last night. . . . I spent the morning writing — to send to all those centres of the P.E.N. we can still reach, so that they can put it about — a letter addressed to that conscience of the world which, when the Czechs wrote to it, was so comfortably absent. I understand now why they wrote at all. Addressing it to the world, they wrote to themselves, to their mind at the moment when it was to be crushed by the Gestapo thumb, to all the places in their body which were still sensible to a pleasure, a grief, an injustice, coming to them from other peoples. And another thing — I had imagined them doing nothing else but choosing the words for this letter they knew would not be answered, except by themselves. But of course, they had to leave it off in the middle to peel potatoes for lunch or bandage a child's knee or run out to pick chives or, suddenly recalling it, alter a sentence in the manuscript pushed aside the morning when it became clear that there was no time to finish anything — except just this useless letter

To the Conscience of the World

*

30 May. My German translator — the woman who used to

translate into German a few of my books, and has been a refugee
since long before the war — came here today and implored me
volubly to go to America. Why did she make this journey only
to warn me, me, that when the country is invaded and, she
implied, taken, I shall be put in a concentration camp or
murdered ? She is equally in danger. It was because she is
tired of running away. . . . " I ran to Italy in 1933 and here
in 1937, I can't run any farther. But you must go — " she
began weakly to cry — " you English don't understand, you
don't believe you're in danger. You don't know."

The more she wept and argued, the harder I grew — and
the more sure that we shall fight. It must look — to these poor
devils, and perhaps to neutrals — as though we are going to
be punished at last for our crimes, our immoral hatred of war,
and our reluctance to begin fighting. Some of them, perhaps,
are not sorry, they think it will take us down a peg. Even our
allies. The French especially, who believe that to reason clearly
is to be wise, must expect our defeat to follow theirs — and
what a consolation ! But wait, wait, my friends — we may
even go up a peg.

I tried to comfort my German friend. I told her that there
are moments where logic and intelligence are less reliable weapons
than plain stupidity. We are too stupid to see what must be
clear to the rest of the continent.

" You are living — and crying into your tea," I said, " on
a corner of Europe which knows more about human freedom
than about logic. . . ."

May I be forgiven the boast. But I am tired of reciting our
sins. Which nation will praise us if we do not, once a decade,
praise ourselves ? It is time now.

*

1 June. Nothing, no moment, in any of our lives can equal
this one. For days we have thought of our men, trapped, driven
to their last hold, almost in sight of us. The thought has eaten
at our tables, stood by our beds, and waited for us when we fell
asleep so that its were the first eyes we saw, fixed on ours. And
they have escaped. All the world knows how. What it doesn't

know, what no one, except ourselves, ever will know, is this storm in us of relief, pride, joy. They are home. We have them.

Nothing will make us afraid again. No more doubts, no fears. It is not a victory. It is deliverance. O infinitely greater, and small enough to be held secretly in the hand — until daylight.

*

15 June. This evening when I came into the kitchen, my sister was setting the trays for breakfast in the morning. She looked at me and smiled. You forget, about the people you live with, that they are beautiful. I felt a slight shock of surprise and pleasure. How hard it is to describe, using only words, the red and white of cheeks (she reminds me of the tale of Snow-white and Rose-red), the colour of eyes which become deeper and brighter at certain moments of a life, the quickness of a young body. Children escaped from hers without marring or making it slower. She is all neat swift energy and impatience. It is hard to believe she will age — ever.

Today I finished writing Cousin Honoré. For the first time for many years — since we took this large house together in the year before the war — I have been writing almost easily. And often, in spite of the war, happy — especially on fine days when I look up from my manuscript and see the trees in the orchard quivering with light, or the tassels of lilac move slowly in answer to some pull, invisible, of the roots sunk in the grass. My sister runs this household — the one thing I always hated — of two families, and I have only to do certain tasks. Which is no burden at all. I am free, as I have never been free. It is worth the drawbacks of this house and way of living.

*

Never has Europe been so near as now, when it is leaving us. You could think it leaned back and brushed lightly now our hands, now a throat from which the voice will spring. And wherever it touches, a shock passes through our nerves to give life to a memory. To the Europe we have lived. Yesterday the Germans bombed Mantes — Mantes-la-Jolie . . . In the summer evening the Seine, running lightly, is grey-green, the colour of sage, except just the moment where a single curve reflects the last yellow of the sunset. Now look from the bridge to the small island, in mid-stream, the Île-aux-Dames, dragging at its double cable of tall poplars behind a line of willows, spectral, their colour buried. A path circles the island behind the poplars. Walk, it is dark now, towards the old house. Look across the wide courtyard to the flight of steps leading to the doorway, and the light from within profiles two figures, mediaeval or a scene from a ballet. You may even know that it is a youth hostel and that in daylight the bare shapely legs, the delicacy, the air of plumes, will become the blouse, shorts, and muscular calves of two girls : the enchantment, at this hour, remains. Leave the island and walk back — do you know what day this is ? — to the Place de l'Hôtel de Ville. France is this small square, paved with cobblestones, the shabby Hôtel de Ville, the trestle-tables outside two small cafés, the Renaissance fountain, dry, shabby, neglected, against which two boys have made with branches an arbour to play a concertina and drum for the young citizens of Mantes-la-Jolie to dance on the worn stones : at the wooden tables the others look on, and drink — what are they drinking ? this is the fourteenth of July 1939.

*

17 June. I went this afternoon to buy wood. Some village women were waiting outside the man's cottage where we buy it. They talked a little, and calmly, about the French surrender. None of them doubted we should go on fighting alone — they did not even speak of it — but one said " They should send the children away now." On the wireless Churchill's short grim speech. Thank God, he made no appeal to America. How well he knows us at this moment, and that we should have felt humiliated and less certain. Before going to sleep I read the terrible sixth chapter of 2 Kings. I always believed that the strength coming from it was clearer than the horror. Now I know.

18 June. It was only half-past five when I woke — and thought instantly, *Ils nous lâchent.* An amazing exultance seized me, like that other early morning when, not expecting them, I saw the Alps affronting the window. That great *Doh* piercing the air (and my body) is unrepeatable, but the sense now of being alone — not yet isolation — prolongs it in this curious echo.

The earth is dry and cracked, the grass burned out. Today, as every day for weeks, the sun flames in the sky like a comet. There are going to be nectarines, dozens of them, on the tree against the wall, and the plum-trees have already more green fruit than leaves. Turning her back on us, France is bequeathing us a summer. Very kind. It would be kinder still if she sent us her Fleet.

30 June. Still the drought, heat, gross dazzling clouds, made fast above blue gulfs. Coming in gusts, a dry wind. We are still waiting, and surely it cannot be put off many more days, or a month, for Hitler to attack England. The soldiers here are making a deep wide moat across the fields, and places at the side of the lane for machine-guns. One of the village women, looking at the barricades, cross-pieces of wood and barbed wire, at the side of our road, said to me, "They look sadly home-made." They do, too. . . . It occurred to me that I should destroy the letters people have written to me and I have kept — I keep very few, those which gave me something. If we are defeated, or only if we are invaded, and the Gestapo came here, the writers of the letters would be compromised. Is this absurd? I don't think it is. So many of the refugees I have tried to help were more obscure than I am, yet they suffered and caused others to suffer : the Gestapo uses a fine net.

With a little grief, I tore up and burned, on the garden bonfire, the small packet of letters from the tallboy. But, just as if it were a trick of my mania for destroying — I destroy everything finished with, letters, papers, manuscripts ; if I could not get rid any better way of clothes and chipped cups I would destroy them : I destroy all half-broken things, to put them out of their misery — a trick to get possession of me, I went on to drag out of my bookshelves all my books on foreign affairs, world politics, economics, sociology, all the neat piles of pamphlets. Rage seized me at the thought that I had wasted so much of my life and reason on them. I threw them on the bonfire. Which went out. I had to light it again several times with branches as dry as the books. I have tortured my mind to understand these things, when it might have been humbly reading Racine or learning to read Greek. What a fool. What a misguided mistaken fool.

My love of destroying is odd, since I keep, and wilfully or with remorse, more useless memories than most people. Of many rooms in which the drowning glance hesitates, of lace curtains chosen by my mother to admit light but no glances even of friends, roads which became habits or a dream, departures when nothing of the long voyage need or could be foreseen by the child, grief of a young man no longer alive, long coarse grass bleached by the salt wind, the tray, lacquered, square with deep sides, used on birthdays to hold the presents, the few moments when happiness, or it may as easily be shame, fixed its image in the mind with a clear colourless acid. I keep all these, but tear up as if I hated it every document which should remind me of the past or has something in it of my life.

As soon as I had finished destroying, the balance dipped on the other side and I began to make a list of things I should like — supposing I too became a refugee, like these Poles and Czechs who are coming here now, from France, and had time to take anything at all — to save. . . . It is not true that I never save anything. Turning out an old despatch-case I found in it the very little bags, size of a small purse, I made from a piece of white calico, and marked them in indelible ink : Rent and Rates ; Coal, Light and Gas ; Food ; Savings ; Clothes, etc. etc. This was in the second year of the last war, in my first, and detested house. The sum divided monthly between them was about ten pounds. You can imagine the virgin flatness of the bag marked Savings. It is in this time, in those days when five hours of profound sleep divided into lengths a torrent of energy, that I place the moment where time turned on itself, and from flowing endlessly, in a young light, began that sudden withdrawal which at an altered speed, but irresistible, it has never relaxed. How foolish they look, these small calico money-bags, with the draw-tapes meant to keep safe their few shillings, and never able to prevent Food being in debt at the end of the month to Payments on Furniture. They may have thought, since they were survivors, the only ones, of a time before time, that they would outlive me. But see, I'm going to burn them, with all the rest.

*

My deep failure is that I finished nothing. I did not bring any of the stages of my life to an end, so that it died richly and naturally into another. I ran away. Always. Leaving them broken off, like green branches thrown down to wither. No, nothing was ever finished. Is there anything I can do now with this rest of my life ? If I could turn it into one book worth writing, or even a few lines. . . . For that one needs a discipline, a force of concentration and the giving up of self, which is very rare ; if I could have contained it I should have behaved in that way from the beginning. I was too ordinary and coarse-meshed. I had been given the strength to form and send out a child after giving him all, all, a mother can give a child. But for this too I lacked discipline and attentiveness, and gave too much because I had withheld, and wasted, part.

*

3 July. These single German planes, loosing their bombs blindly in the country, are the first pattering drops of the rain which has drenched Europe. Everything behaves as if a downpour were expected. Even the cloud of starlings which this morning rose, in the single thunder of wings followed by a shower of cries, from all the trees at the edge of the heath — it was because above them a hawk hung motionless. And even the magpies — one, two, then a second pair — springing in a sudden curve from the tallest elm, as if released by a lever. These hazards, at any other time signs, peaceable and modest, of a spring under the wrinkled surface of life, are today the fears, the pleasure, of war. There are a few minutes left. The cloud, with these first heavy drops, is lower. . . . Last night's bombs were our first. I woke and was out of the bed and running to the night nursery in the same moment as the distant firing, coming suddenly nearer — as though salutes were being fired at points along the route of a procession — reached our guns, behind the village. . . . Why did I snatch up Judy rather than Nicholas ? . . . He was sitting up in bed and asked in a calm voice, " What is that noise ? " — " Nothing," I said : " only the bangs. You know. . . ." I carried her, still asleep, downstairs and gave her to N. to take to the cellar. Going back I met my brother-in-law carrying Nicholas ; behind them, with the attaché-case where she keeps the housekeeping money, neatly in separate little boxes, my sister. I had meant to go down again to the cellar, but seen from my window the searchlights were so fine I could not leave them. The others stayed for a few minutes in the cellar, then went back to bed and to sleep. It was absurdly silly, because the bombs had been dropped, harmlessly in the fields, when I was on the stairs with the sleeping child — not that we knew then where they had dropped — but we have had no experience. . . . It only seemed natural — almost a habit.

What happened this morning was not so easy to accept. The clouds were very low, and a single German machine flew out of them, as suddenly as one of yesterday's magpies, thundered over the house and dropped his bombs more than a mile away. Nicholas ran in from the garden, very pale. He did not want to go out again, and suddenly two of his four years of changing and growing dropped from him ; he went upstairs and came down with a small flannel blanket he used to adore when he was a child, and prepared to roll himself up in it on the floor, with the fingers of his left hand in his mouth, another habit of that time.

In a too casual voice he said, " I feel like playing in the house this morning."

His mother drove him out into the garden — as you make a child ride home after a fall from his horse.

How gently he is still treating us. The dead children of Poland and the other countries which know him better than we do would find a smile for this innocent murderer. We watch him closely, and all we notice is one finger, lifted slightly, or the scarcely perceptible movement of a foot. It is a little unnerving. But I am not one of those who cry, " Anything is better than this suspense ! " No, no — anything is better than another dead child. Than one. . . .

I am reading the charmingly urbane letters written by Harriet Cavendish between 1796 and 1809. They could equally well have been written before the fall of Nineveh — nearer to it than to us.

*

They come into my room through the closed door, and watch me write letter after letter. There is already a heap of letters at the end of the table, and more to be written. It is nearly midnight : my eyelids have had to be propped up by two thorns. If it were not for their supervision I would stop tearing words from *le terrain avare et froid de ma cervelle*. The letters are to other people about them, or to the Home Office, or to themselves about themselves and about each other. One has written about her interned husband — I answer her and write about him to the Home Office. Another, not interned yet, wants advice and to be encouraged. A third who is interned will need four letters to his own cheek.

And it is all unnecessary. None of this folly, wickedness, suffering, need have happened, if it were not that men have an invincible habit of tormenting each other. Why ? Have they so few ways of proving to themselves that they are alive ?

I persuade myself that if I were interned I should keep quiet, and discuss with myself my self. But then I have never been interned, nor am I haunted by the fear that one fine morning the Germans will arrive and I shall be handed over to them — as it happened in France. I remind myself of this when I am on the point of being exasperated by the insistence of these victims on surviving.

Why I am working all night is that I have been in London all the day. I went there to talk to the person on whom they really depend. For one exiled writer who turns to me, twenty throw themselves on the humanity and deep wisdom of the secretary of the P.E.N., without dreaming that he will not be able to give up his whole time to each of them. You could think that Hermon Ould had spent the years when he was knotting the threads of this society — in every knot the capital of a country — preparing them to take this strain. He is holding together the meshes of what has after all become a net for saving lives. Today he looked completely exhausted. At one moment, when a German writer came in with a scheme that would involve us in raising five hundred pounds at once, we were seized by an insane laughter, which we passed off to him as influenza. A strange disease, which attacks without warning and causes tears to pour down the patient's face. . . . I remembered that I had promised to visit the Rudolf Oldens. They are in the flat they were lent when he came out of internment. On the way there I was surprised when without the least warning it grew dark. An eclipse ! I said to myself. . . . My sight cleared. I was holding to the railings of an area — as though what I really expected was an earthquake. . . . When I came into the room, Rudolf's wife, the composed quiet Ika, nodded at me with a distracted look. She was telephoning to a doctor, and trembling — when she had to wait for the answer she forced her teeth together to prevent their chattering. "Don't go," she said, "Rudi is ill, he has collapsed. I think you can help — you comforted us so often."

She went out of the room, and in a moment came back to say he wanted to talk to me. . . . He was lying in bed on his side, his face grey under its film of sweat. He smiled a little, and held his hand out, stammering an apology for being ill ; suddenly a convulsion seized him, he covered his face with his hands and sobbed, between violent jerks of his body. I fled from the room. . . . When I had seen him last, in April, he believed that some use was going to be made of his knowledge and intelligence : at last. But after ignoring him, we suddenly interned them with him — with the effect I had seen. . . . Ika came back — and now, she was again in herself and looked out at me with calm.

"What did they do to him in the camp ?"

"He is delicate. It was one of the bad camps. He suffered." She added, reflecting, "But that was nothing. It was his disappointment — to be thrown out——"

"What can I do ?"

" Nothing . . . unless you would go and look at some flats for me. You see, we have to leave here tomorrow — sooner than I thought."

I wrote down the names. In the streets it was hotter than ever, so hot that the houses seemed swollen. I went from one place to the next. They were all dreadful. I was ashamed, because I had not found a place for Ika, of my exhaustion. I rang her up. She had just heard that they would be allowed the flat for another week — " and by then perhaps, we shall know whether we can stay in England, or if we must accept this offer. You knew that Columbia University has offered to make him a professor ? Of German history." She added in her usual calm voice, " We have been here six years. Until this year we didn't know we were not wanted."

" Don't judge us by our moments of panic," I said, and rang off. . . .

But is it panic ? Or the sudden widening, into an abyss of meanness, of a crack none of us had noticed ? It is true we have an excuse. There may be a fifth columnist or two among the Germans and Austrians, and we have seen what damage a fifth column can do. But in the Dutch, the Belgian, the French fifth columns, how many aliens ? Fifty ? Ten ? One ? . . . It angers me that England should fall into this obscene panic. The war ? It is not every day that one has such an excuse for practising the virtues of firmness — towards the helpless. So my country can only save itself by hurrying sons and husbands out of the country, without a word, until they are gone, to the frantic women ? And, when a ship-load of them is drowned, by declaring that all those on board were Nazis ? It is a lie. . . . Stupidity ? Incompetence ? . . . I am ashamed.

I must sleep. . . . In a clear sky, the searchlights fold and open a fan, closing and dilating the intervals between the transparent rods. At last the closed fan is held motionless, upright, the halting sound of aeroplanes ceases below the horizon, and this sound I hear is only the too noisy beating of my heart — calling attention to itself. What unsatisfied hope is keeping, close to me, these patient shadows ? I must sleep. Look — look at all the letters I have written about you. . . . *I have, Sir, the honour to be Your obedient servant. . . .* True, they will do none of you any good.

*

Yesterday, we invited the exiled writers again — including a few Germans who have not been interned. Old Dr. Federn, the historian, so old, so brave, so gay, and like a grasshopper in his shabby frock-coat, talked to me about another German he wants to save from internment. Until I spoke of him myself, he did not mention his delicate son who is interned, and then he said quickly, with his smile, " You are not to mind. England is the best people in the world — and kind." Another German listened, an old gentle creature, a philologist and translator of Shakespeare, now modestly starving in the country he, because of this same Shakespeare, thinks of as his home.

There was a Czech poet, young, severe — out of reserve or pride he stood the whole evening alone, mutely refusing himself to every current ; there were also Poles — among them a young man who related in a polite voice, with gestures almost smiles, the stages by which a country is forced in a few short months to relive the Dark Ages, by pillage, the destruction of libraries, the murder of scholars ; and there was a distinguished Polish novelist, Marja Kuncewiczowa, whose laboured English did not succeed in hiding a subtle and elegant mind. What can one say to these writers who have lost not only their country but their language ? How can Madame Kuncewiczowa live when her hand, her delicate writing - hand, has been cut at the wrist ? Exiled from two countries at once, Poland and literature, she can keep herself alive only by the passion of her belief that she exists. I looked at her. Yes, she exists. She is charming, her face has the clearness and lightness of an ivory, each of its fine bones is a vow—not to die, and to speak Polish, always Polish. . . . Leaning against the buffet, an elderly Frenchman, a journalist, talked for a long time to one of the Czechs. I was avoiding them, but the Czech caught my arm. " What are we to do with the pure-bred Nazis, the real young thugs ? " he said. He looked at me with a little malice.

" I don't know."

" Kill them," the Frenchman said.

" Exactly my idea ! And listen. Little as I want to give up any of our land — I have been a farmer longer than I am a soldier or a writer — I would cut off three narrow strips of Czechoslovakia and get rid that way of two out of our three million Boches. Of the million left, half will be killed before I get there. A pity. . . . The rest can be given their choice of going to Germany with their goods and their metaphors — we are not thieves and we have real poets — or becoming Czechs. No more German schools, no double faces, no politicians who are traitors, and teachers of gymnastic who mean to murder some of their pupils. This time — finish ! "

The Frenchman half closed his eyes, to see better inside them. " I believe," he said drily, " there will not be a German problem. There will be, when the Germans are retreating, another Night of the Long Knives. They think, these ordures, that they have taken France without paying. Every minute adds to the debt."

Certainly I understand it. I understand these dreams the colour of hate, and the wish to strangle — the hands of the Czech who used to be a farmer had arranged themselves with just room for a neck — and to blot out eyes which saw the dead children and the hostages with their bandaged glance. And yet this darkness, this second night of Europe, stifles me. It is not the dead, not these hands already like roots, who insist that debts must be paid. No bailiffs among them. Only silence and indifference. Who will blame the living if they assume the anger, hate, justice, of these' who feel nothing, not even the cold of the earth ? And will dare promise them that they need not spend the rest of their lives with the taste of their justice ?

" You disapprove of us ! " the Czech said to me.

" Not at all. You know what you want — where we, with a different experience, are increasingly uncertain. That's always something. You have only to find out whether you enjoy what you want."

It seemed to me that our German guests needed attention more than the others. They have a habit of standing about in groups — close to them, the country they can't touch. I can only listen — and listen — and become nothing.

*

2 August. The house, without the children, is deathly quiet. The sense has gone out of the orchard and kitchen-garden where they ran and shouted and cried.

After the French surrender, and when the defences against invasion were being improvised in the roads and lanes, in that motionless heat — and other children had gone — we thought of sending ours to the States or Canada. I doubted whether there were time. But we took the first steps in a maze of formalities — and I wrote to America. A terrible struggle began in my sister's mind during these weeks. In her body, since her children are nerves of her life, and dear possessions of a young woman as firmly possessive as any of ours. Can there be any more frightful riddle than the one English mothers are being asked? They are being given time to ask themselves : If I keep my child with me, am I handing it to its butchers? And if after all we are not invaded, what have I done? . . . Like the others, my young sister had to decide, quickly, whether to save her two she ought to give them up.

She is entirely her husband and children — as you can say that a spring is its cool freshness. She has no joys or ambitions which are not their image. The courage to give them up has been taken from her veins. Rightly, her husband left the decision to her. I say rightly, because in my family it is the mother who decides such things. And, too, it is her days which will change, and become unbalanced by the loss of her children.

It was not one, but several Americans — friends, the friends of friends, and women who only knew me by name — who offered to take our two. Who will say enough about America at this time? There are no words for so reckless a generosity, and the pure goodness of Americans who write : Your children need not risk the fate of Polish children — send them to us. It is not possible to reckon our debt, still less pay it. They are strange people, these Americans. You and your wars, they say ; don't ask us to help you ! And in the same breath : Let us help you. They have none of that tact which makes such a handsome mask for a mean egoism, they boast of what is least admirable — its gadgets — in their civilisation, and keep a modest silence about its spirit, which is young enough to afford mistakes. When we English say of them, as we do, "They don't know they've been born," we are speaking about their greatest good fortune. . . .

Nothing, my sister said, would keep her out of England : she will take them over, then come back. When I told her that might not be easy, she was vexed : "They can't forbid me to come home," she said : "what nonsense !" I hope so.

They left last night to take the night train to Liverpool. We put the children to bed early, at five, and at half-past eight woke them ; they had to leave the house at nine. Nicholas's energy and good-temper woke with him, but Judy was furiously sleepy and fought against being dressed. When the luggage was being piled into the car I took her up — she was crying with rage — and carried her about the garden, while Nicholas went through all his tricks to amuse her. . . . "Look, Judy, look at me. . . ."

An evening like any other evening in summer, full of light and penetrated by a breath of darkness. A long way off, the sound of an aeroplane — at its height, its pilot probably saw at least a splinter of the continent where cruelty can do as it likes, where it is no longer a crime to open up a child's body and leave it to die at the side of the road, where men exert themselves to give death and pain, as if life had become worthless. The sky was very clear. The moment when I lifted the child into the car stretched back endlessly, fastening itself to the mistakes and griefs of the past. Surely this is right, I thought ; surely it is wrong. My young sister — who never cries — was making as she cried the same face she made when she was a child.

"Don't try to keep me over there," she said to me, "they don't need me so much as *he* does."

You cannot think what this house is like today, without them. Imagine in your life a day when you learned that the one person you were reckless enough to depend on has betrayed you, when to every real act of ill-faith or ridicule you add a cloud of imagined ones, so that your mind is flayed and every touch on it is an anguish, and when you realise at last that yourself, by your childish need, as exigent as a child's, to be loved, has betrayed yourself — you will form some idea of the emptiness in these rooms and this orchard.

If I stretch myself, I can hold the house together. I can't give it its living soul. That at this moment is lodged in some part of a ship in the Mersey. They have still to cross safely.

*

This morning, the cool air, promising warmth, and the acrid smell of wood-smoke, opened round me suddenly the air, mediaeval, of a Spanish village — of the coast village north of Barcelona where we lived one March and April, it was five years ago. So small — a harbour, behind it the few narrow streets, thick in dust, the dry hills — but three worlds, each with its climate, customs, even its own time. There was the hotel, simply a large Catalan house, renovated, but that could not change its air of detesting the sun — owned and run by a foreigner — Swiss ? German ? The guests, speaking every language except Spanish, set their watches by the wireless, so that their time was strictly that of March 1935. Its waves had swept here — together with a few touring cars, newspapers sent by post and arriving, since they had become involved in the indefinitely stretched-out Spanish time, like the light of extinct stars, with their excite-ment about events already out of sight — a school of young female artists. Their trousers were not indecent — what made them seem to be was the air of charade given them by bangles, rouge, purple toe-nails. And the loud English laughter, a gramophone needle jerked brutally across the record. They chattered and lounged at the tables in the narrow courtyard with its wind-bitten orange-tree and single gaunt waiter, a Catalan. One of the other guests, the French business man on holiday with his mistress, asked him if he admired them. The Catalan distorted one side of his face, the eyelid sinking as the corner of his mouth rose — and it was the face of Dürer's Death which so distorted itself ; he had the same severe elegance and as little flesh. The guests did not try to plague him as they plagued with their exactions and absurd troubles the patient little Jewish secretary and dog-of-all-work, less a human being than the voice, soothing, gentle, of an immense fatigue — and an immense lie : no one is really a block of abnegation and friendly smiles.

All this whirring polyglot life, always glancing at a watch to see whether it were time to leave the beach for the hotel or the hotel for the only and poor café, was isolated from the bare mediaeval life of the village : ironical silence, poverty, of Catalan fishermen, of peasants turning over by hand a few feet of cracked earth full of stones, impenetrable houses, children with skeletal hands playing in the dust between the buttresses of the large church, the clumsy body of the parish priest. In their black heavy clothes, and unsmiling, the Catalan women watched young women in trousers or bare-backed sauntering along the streets on their way to bathe. Could they even see each other ? — moving, as they did, in moments so completely separate, not even of the same kind. Nothing was reflected, from the silence, the poverty and inflexible dignity and ignorance of the one on to the glittering indignity of the other. You could not say that the hotel and its guests were a foreign growth in the village. They were not attached to it in any way, even as a tumour ; the slightest movement would shake them off.

But there was a, so to speak, mediating life between these two. That was the life led by a few German refugees who had settled in the village. Here, where baker or chemist always offered his cheapest goods first, their little money would go farther than anywhere in western Europe. Living though they were in the past, it was a past nearer to the time of the foreign hotel, and they were able to understand this and make use of it. One among them would be employed by a visitor as chauffeur, or holiday tutor. Or a German Jew who had established himself, as a dentist perhaps, in Barcelona, would come to the hotel, and for a few evenings his countrymen ate there as guests, worried by the sarcastic politeness of Death in his shape of a Catalan waiter.

For a few hours during the day, the sun was hot ; a blinding light sprang between the sea, which remained icy, and the houses placed like white stones between sea and hills. The instant the sun sank below the hills the air became cold. There was, too, a dry wind like a scythe, which covered everything with fine dust. It started a nervous tension at the back of the eyes and in the muscles, exasperating.

Even on windless days it was too cold in the late afternoon except to walk. One April day at half-past five, when we set out, the sun was lowering itself behind the hills ; its hair streamed triumphantly upward, a long glittering tuft. We climbed across the land side of a headland, the track dry and steep, slopes where the soil had hardened into fantastic organ-pipes, dry noise of cicadas, everywhere flowering heaths, the air scented by them. Nowhere except in these bare hills have I breathed such perfume. The sun, when we reached the top of the hill, had been shaken out, but the light glowed for several minutes. We followed the path — difficult with gaps and stones — round the headland. Suddenly the sea, in flower ; the sardine boats were all out and they carry powerful acetylene stern lamps. The path went on without end between the ghostly plants, their brittle life gone off in scent — on, then down, down. Will it drop to the unseen coast road ? In a stony gully it began climbing again a further headland. We left it and plunged down in darkness, slipping, clutching at roots ; when we fell on to the road and turned to walk back to the village, the sea, on our left, was in full darkness, the many lights resting on it like sea-birds, those farther off gently ruffled, the nearer sending ripples of light to run on the rocks still far below the road ; a crescent moon ; lights of a passenger-ship going south, the knuckles of a hand gripping the horizon. The road climbed and turned. The descent to the village ; the night chorus of frogs, rising through every least vein of the darkness, inexorably ; the beam of the lighthouse sending out letter by letter a word made up of sea, cliff, road. The streets were empty, and the light escaping from a half-shuttered window was ironical in its insistence on cold and solitude. My room, with its bare walls and stone floor under the matting, was cold, and the stove only filled it with the bitter smoke of wood, so bitter that I knew I should recall it.

*

England is — we spend so much effort to conceal our ignorance of England, that ignorance which earns us the ill-will of foreigners, who put it down to complacence or vanity, although the truth, that England is a boy shot down in the air above his own fields and an old woman ending her days in the trifling joys and squabbles of an almshouse, is too simple to compromise with any of those superb abstractions in free use in other countries, and too heavy, so that it can scarcely squeeze itself into the bee-hive — so why should I not say that England, among all the other persons she is, is that thin unabatable old lady, my aunt, my mother's sister ? As my mother was, she is a part of the town, with its mud-filled harbour, its cramped streets. But she never left it. All the voyages of her lively mind have the form of one or other of its streets, and if her eyes, blue, clouded, could give back the images pressed into them, the first and last would be that of the Parish Church shepherding its old effaced tombstones on the edge of the cliff : she looks at it from her window, across the roofs and the harbour, in every light, from the youngest to that dying gold which clings to it with such fond love. She looks at it — but does not go inside ; as you would guess, she belongs, as did my mother, to the sect which descends from Cromwell's Independents. No one could be more true in spirit, or slighter in body, or more fearless. You can see her — in all her seventy-odd years she has not learned to tell lies ; I fear it is too late — in the letters she has written me this month.

". . . things are dreadfully scarce here, and now there are no Matches to be got, I don't know what we are coming to, if you want anything at all you have to spend the whole day in the streets, we had 2 hectic nights last week, with these disgraceful bombs, I had to take shelter in the coal-house passage which the Warden, poor fellow, assures me is the safest place. What we do at these times ! . . ."

". . . it is just possible you may know we have been bombed this afternoon, and I am writing to tell you that we are *all serene*. We supposed it was one of our own Planes, it was going so quickly and just over the house-tops ; we were watching it out of the sitting-room window when, without a word, there was a blinding flash and a loud terrible noise, and we fled downstairs for our lives. And afterwards, O the destruction ! I never thought the Germans would sink *so* low or that I should live to see the town in this state. I have just remembered that it is your Parent's birthday tomorrow. The last time I saw him I was not able to conceal my disgust with the pleasure he takes in pretending that nothing I mention is important — whether it is the War or a fine day. We shall see whether it is nothing that four of his own windows have been blown in. Mine, I am thankful, are not touched. . . ."

*

The stunted little mechanic, returning this evening from the East End to his R.A.F. station somewhere in the country. He talked only to explain to himself the anguish he felt. It puzzled him. It was too large for him, he struggled to fit it into himself and it broke open on all sides like an ill-made parcel. He had a slight squint, which gave him the air of seeking in himself the reason of his anguish. " Seems a silly way of making war. You hit me and I'll hit you. I reckon they ought to stop it . . . you know, it's the women and kids. . . . My wife, now, she has the baby in the shelter every night, all night, and then three or four raids a day, she can't bath him even, as soon as she's had breakfast and begun washing him, the siren goes. . . . When you say goodbye their heart's in their boots, you can see it. . . . Of course you couldn't do any good if you were with them, but they'd feel better. . . ." To be travelling away from danger, leaving his family under the threat of German bombs — what an extreme triumph of the social instinct. It fought in him with the instinct to stay with his own, to place his thin body, spoiled by a slum, between them and the weight of their death. What orders we obey for the sake of obeying. I could do nothing for him except listen. I did that, hiding my dislike of an unhappiness which must talk. Or I had given all my futile pity to one of the two soldiers in the carriage — a boy. On the platform, to see him off, he had two women ; his mother, shabby, her hands worn and cracked, made towards him timid signs he ignored : all his eyes were for his girl who was with her, made up to resemble, grossly, a film star. He looked at her and repeated, "I'll be back." His effort brought drops of sweat to his forehead. As soon as the train started, he glanced with a vague smile at the other soldier and said softly, "That's over." While his friend slept, he sorted his photographs of her from the letters in a new pocket-book.

*

This morning in London I walked through one of those zones, or rays, of pure happiness through which this planet passes at irregular and always unpredictable moments. Or no one has learned yet how to predict them. I was opposite Westminster Abbey when the line of longitude I was walking on passed through the ray. There was a light wind. The sky, a pale blue, broke into white foam over the roof. A tune slipped from the past and played itself on a hurdy-gurdy waiting at a sunny corner for just such a piece of luck. What use is it to be poor, modest, if you cannot in these moments squander your last, absolutely the last, reserve of youth and irresponsible freedom? Moments of escape — but where? — from this nightmare, this iron sky closing on us. . . . What use to feel cold if not to smile at these London trees warm in a light the colour of honey and silence?

I bought an evening paper and read that the *City of Benares* has been torpedoed. She was carrying children and all but a few of them are lost. The air now was glacial. And already my eye had seen another name, and I leaned, to read it, against the nearest wall. The Oldens were on board and are both lost. An English officer tried to force Ika into one of the boats, but she refused to go without her husband : who was too ill. . . . But I can hear the voice, even, quiet, deep, and the very few words with which she refused. . . . *I can't leave Rudi. I'm sorry.* . . . I am sure that is what she said ; she would be unyielding and softly polite, regretful that she had to be disobliging — and immovable. In her young face the dark eyes would not waver.

This was why you came to England, my dear Rudi, with your hatred of cruelty and tyranny and your passion for truth, the two fires which burned your flesh so that even your smile was twisted, as though from within. I watched you at an international committee, with Jules Romains, and a Polish writer of whom nothing has been heard since, waiting with this half-eager, half-ironical smile, to remind the Frenchman that the Nazis have murdered or exiled all the good German writers and this simple fact is the only one a writer need remember about them. But you remembered much more. As scholar, as liberal humanist, you could not forget what was going on in the night of barracks and concentration camps. And how eagerly you believed in our English freedom.

You had time, even before the war, to remember our English dislike of intelligence. . . . What would you have done, my friend, without your wife's smiling calm, without that limitless devotion she placed so quietly, unnoticed, in your hands ? You had that. And the little lively child, born here — " the English subject," Ika said, smiling. . . .

I have one of the letters Rudolf wrote to me when the internments began here. It had occurred to him that, if we asked them, the American writers might press their Government to invite German writers living in France and England — he had the strangest idea of the value of writers. When he was strongly moved, his English became very bad ; you could judge his feelings by the state of his tenses — " . . . no one, I feel certain, would wish to give the appearance as if he ran away from dangers. I should say almost all of these writers living in France or here would have had the possibility to go to the United States in past years and they remained deliberately in Europe although they with certainty foresaw the war. Some of them only wanted to remain nearer the decision, some of them did it for love to Europe, some felt sure he would be used in information or broadcasting work and wanted to fight the Nazi. This was perhaps foolish but it was so. You see : this is a ridiculous situation. They remained here to work and they are thoroughly been stifled. (To work or fight they thought by their voice.) The trouble of being interned is not so much this to live for some time without the usual comfort and liberty — but it is : to be entirely idle whilst one hoped for utter activity. Further on it means that especially those writers who are of the Allies' cause and could be use for it will be useless. I should like to suggest to look on their case from the political angle and not from a humanitarian one. I do not think it would be the moment for considerations of this latter kind. . . . What great, rare, reassuring, comforting occurrence that I can write this to you. . . ."

To humiliate a man like Olden it is not necessary to shut him up in a disused cotton mill, bare and verminous. That was extravagant.

He hoped until the last minute that the English would keep him. Until the very last, when they were going on board . . . there would be a telegram ; the Travelling Paper, where the clause allowing him to return was crossed through again and again thickly, in red ink, was a mistake — You are wanted in England. . . . " I regret," he wrote the night before he sailed, " to leave this country in this moment. But no choice was left to me. Please, do not forget our unhappy comrades in the camps — when there will be more calm than it is now. And do not forget us."

It seems to me that many people will remember a distinguished writer we humiliated. I ought to remember his young smiling wife. She was always, except that one time, stubborn and gentle, composed and gay, calm and smiling. Even when, because of the internments, she decided to send Kutzi, who was two years old, to a friend in Canada. . . .

" At the English passport office they gave me a passport for her at once, and they were very kind. Then I thought : Perhaps she has to go through the States. Very well, this morning I went to the American consulate, to show them her English passport and ask : Suppose she needs it, will you give her a visa ? But they have a man there in the hall who is simply brutal. He asked : What's the passport ? — She is a British subject, I said. — Parents' nationality ? — As soon as I told him : Stateless, he said : Nothing for you here, and I'll tell you right away we don't grant visas on compassionate grounds. — But I'm not asking you for compassion, I came to make enquiries. — Nothing doing. You can try again at 9.30 tomorrow if you want to. . . . Then he pushed me out quickly."

" I'll ask for you," I said : " unkindness of that sort rolls off me."

She refused. " Off me, too. You forget my mother was English," she said, smiling. . . .

A telegram : " Rudi interned. Kutzi left for Toronto ". . . . The police who came for him comforted her, and she forced herself to be grateful for a politeness which alarmed her more than the thought of her empty house. Then, as the door shut, the emptiness sprang at her. This cottage they had lived in for four years was an enemy ; it had hidden one of Kutzi's shoes and chose this moment to drop it in front of her ; and when she had to make a list of the papers the police had taken away with them — these included Kutzi's birth certificate — her hands shook and everything she touched slipped from them.

For a week or two longer she kept up a pretence that this was an interruption, not the end, of their life here. But the house itself, in all the ways a house can be malignant, forced the truth on her. She gave in, without panic, and came to live in London, where it would be easier to work for Rudi. And for the others her loyalty did not forget when she was only thinking of him. . . . She never pitied herself, or him — poor vice of exiles. She had only just admitted her exile and she would not flatter it. Each time we met during those weeks when the authorities, moving like men who are frost-bitten, were preparing to release him on condition that he went to America, she spoke as though I had an imaginary grudge against England which she must cure me of. She had a deep voice, with an abruptly silenced vibration, a voice which delighted me. How many times, smiling, she said as if she felt no anxiety, " And when Rudi comes home . . ." It was by chance I learned she was not able to sleep. . . .

Sleep, sleep, brave Ika. You shan't, I promise it, be forgotten.

*

The atmosphere of these days, of waiting, is that of autumn — no rain, but suddenly a feeling of chill, as if the sun had turned its shoulder on us. Over-night, the leaves of the elms have become yellow, the colour of suspense. We listen.

Yesterday evening, I was writing in my room, warm, with the fire, and heard the stuttering noise of a German plane. For a moment, until the bombs fell, a long way off, I felt a sense of comfort and pleasure. Why? Behind what I was writing, my mind groped in the darkness, then suddenly gave me back the sputtering gas-jet in my bedroom when I was a child. How often, waiting for my mother to come upstairs to say good-night and turn it off, I listened to it with ears already drowned under sleep. And then she came in and stooped over the bed, touching my cheek with a lightly roughened finger. . . . Go to sleep now, my good little love. . . . The two sounds, gas-jet and German bomber, are the same. No wonder that our generation is slightly cracked, sullen, or giddy, seeing that it has to hold together two extremities a torrent is trying to force apart. What energy could we possibly have left over for all the other things we should have done, the poems we ought to have written, the children we should have brought up in safe placid houses, the problems — *Sonnant dans l'âme un creux toujours futur* — we should have meditated ? We have all we can do to appear sane. Very often I doubt whether a generation will be born able to stand the terribly accelerated speeds, and the pressure of things spawning from us like numbers in a geometrical nightmare. We may have to renounce them — as the only way of saving ourselves. Open our hands and let drop possessions, haste, even change. What luck, in that time, to be born in a country of vines and olives. . . .

When I was in bed other planes came over, and dropped their bombs about the neighbourhood. There is a new searchlight facing the window nearest my bed ; it lights up the room as it comes round, touching the tallboy, the mirror, my cheek . . . a finger. . . . Nothing is stranger than to lie in bed in the quiet dark of the country, to be roused by bombs, then to listen to the plane drone out of hearing like an insect on a warm day, to sleep, to hear another machine, the guns picking it up, and bombs again, dropped, it seems, into nothing, muffled by the blackness. There is none of the excitement I feel in London, nor the sense of danger. It is, I think, the silence, and the one plane isolated in it. One listens as in a dream. If I don't hear the plane coming, the first bomb startles me, sending an electric shock to the ends of my fingers. Then, the calm sense of a dream comes back. I sleep lightly afterwards, and the next plane wakens me at once. One night this week our cockerel startled me awake, I thought he was a new sort of bomb coming down.

This morning, very early, the sirens woke me. I was surprised and listened drowsily to a succession of sounds in the almost-darkness ; first, that shuddering of the air one hears at night before hearing the plane, then a cock crew, then the planes, other cocks answering the first from all the scattered farms, then bombs, then silence and an owl in the paddock, then far-off gun-fire, the sound of the planes fading . . . a jay called out . . . another. . . . A broad finger of moonlight caressed the bookshelves under the window.

My fear of inner defeat — as of a door which would open silently on the dark stairs — always in me, even when I was confident and greedy — has turned to indifference. What lies beyond defeat ? Wait, wait, you can be sure it is not so bitter.

*

Yesterday morning a German plane unseen above the clouds, grey, heavy, of a day of warm rain, dropped three bombs near the Roman wall. One of them killed a woman in the field with the Saxon name. Another fell between the forgotten church with its memorial tablets and the old charming plain vicarage. In the bomb crater in the field, a boy later picked up a Saxon flint.

*

The house settled on itself again, with a smile of relief, as soon as my young sister returned. It is no use pretending I did more, during these fifteen weeks, than just keep it going ; I did nothing to please it.

She is safe, and I can think over the extreme fear of these days, almost living — it was at my heels on the staircase ; the stair creaked after my foot left it, and when I drew my curtains at night it took the shape of a fold and I lay trying in the dark to out-stare it. . . . Six days ago *The Times* said that a German pocket battleship had attacked a convoy half-way between

Ireland and Newfoundland. We had guessed — when my sister cabled from Chicago to us : *On my way to see Montreal* — that she would sail that week-end. And the day after *The Times* report, when we were reading that " losses in the convoy are likely to be very heavy ", another cable, signed by an unknown name — *Left Sunday.*

In my family we are not given to premonitions, any more than to colds in the head. We expect to survive. I did not recognise it as fear, the restlessness that drove me to walk about the house, to run errands, anything sooner than the effort of giving life to the ghost — it has been waiting about in my mind for months and I was eager to talk to it — of The Fort. If my brother-in-law had said he was anxious I should have deafened him with my reasons for being certain she was safe. To get itself noticed, my fear had to make the crudest signs. . . . The third morning I was dressing — almost in the dark ; I refuse to turn on a light, not only because it jars after the darkness and sleep, but it would mean drawing blinds and curtains, all that annoyance of black-out — when I heard the hoarse cries of wild geese. I ran to the window and flung it up. There they were, flying very fast, dark against a grey sky ruffled by dove-grey clouds. In the east a narrow strait of clear pale yellow. The same, the very same sky I have seen so often at home, but — time is in reverse with me now — at the other end of the day, after sunset. A hand pinched me. I remembered that at home we call the crying of wild geese in flight the gabble-rachet — it is their tally-ho and away as they hunt the newly-dead. . . . I had an anguished thought that her thin body was sinking through icy Atlantic water. . . . At the Canadian Pacific they said they had no news, and so far as they knew their ships did not sail in convoy. . . . But the image persisted, and placed itself wherever I looked. For the next three days it stayed with me, in front of or behind my shoulder ; either its breath or its distorting reflection clouded every mirror. Armistice Day came. The newspapers had a circumstantial report that a Canadian Pacific boat, the *Empress of Japan*, had been bombed and disabled four hundred miles west of Ireland. Why did I believe at once that this must be her boat ? In my plain senses I should easily have convinced myself that it was the last ship she was likely to be in. . . . I rang up N. to ask again at the shipping office in London. While I was waiting for the answer, I remembered the Two Minutes and followed them into that underworld where I have more friends than in this, and — I have none here — a brother. But, for the first time, it was only the past — as if it belonged to my childhood, as if he had died then. He, my mother, that life, that undisciplined girl, are all dead. I am not that girl, and only a few of her acts are able, still, to make me cry out. . . . The telephone rang downstairs, and I rushed to it. For a few seconds my head throbbed so that I could not hear. Then . . . the *Empress of Japan* is not now in the firm's service, and your sister will be on a smaller boat — which is in the Mersey at this moment. . . .

I insulted my fear, and chased it out of my sight with my mother's cruelly sarcastic laugh. Fool ! I shouted — in her very voice. And it has gone. Of course it has gone. And just now I caught myself thinking of it at the end of a passage. This is idiotic. Since it is in the past, why do I think of it in the future ? If my family were not the sanest eccentrics in their part of the country, I should say I was a little touched. . . .

This morning in London, one of my friends asked : " How did your sister get back ? They told me at the passport office that Englishwomen who went to the States will have to stay there, it is impossible to get a boat."

" Ha, it would take more than the Government to keep one of us in America when she wanted to come home," I said.

It was only when my friend looked at me oddly that I saw how foolish my remark was. Do I often, I wonder, make remarks like this ?

It never entered my young sister's head that she would stay in the safety of America. As soon as she had settled her children with their generous foster-parents she set about coming back. She found it would be difficult to come from New York, and so went quickly to Canada and came from there.

She began — the day she arrived — to plan against the children's coming home. She is furnishing a dolls'-house, more modern — it will have electric lighting — but not more likely to be the meeting-place of witty cultivated beings, almost always awake, lolling on their sofas, and talking, interminably, than the one a ship's carpenter made, and my mother furnished . . . even to window-boxes she bought in Antwerp, and mirrors hanging awry, which a child's eagerly clumsy finger could never put straight.

*

Today the sky is a greenish grey, as though it reflected the North Sea. Even though at its height it ought to be able to see two hundred miles, I don't believe it. There is a wind and grey clouds. These, and the leafless branches, each doubled by a line of rain-drops, carry me to the fields behind my mother's house : it is an afternoon in winter, a mist from the sea doubles the sky : always at the same place, where she can look one way to the moors and another to the Church and the Abbey ruins on the edge of the cliff, she pauses. The bare trees, the chill thin air . . . her life and mine go on there, unseen, unending, and these walks, part of the ritual of her life, will never end, even when I do. There will endlessly, in this street, at that turn of the moor road, for those who can feel it, be a footstep doubling theirs, a breath . . . the light pressure on them of a memory not theirs. . . . My aunt writes that they have been bombed again — the bomb fell in the field, always, because we looked at it from the other side of the harbour, smooth, below the Abbey, and in a road nearer the cemetery, and beyond it among the Golden Grove trees. Did they disturb you in your cold sleep, my poor love ? And no daughter to tell you that it was a storm or the armistice guns.

*

1941

13 January. There is nothing clear in the colour of winter moonlight. These last few mornings I have dressed in bright moonlight, at about half-past six. This morning a curiously elongated moon — I should know it again from all the others — woke me at five o'clock by stroking my face. I lay looking at the garden. There was a bird in the long grass. At the other side of the orchard the trees were remote and rather bestial, like some passages in Aeschylus. Although I could see everything, the light was menacing and ambiguous.

I have finished The Fort.

*

The abyss of sadness in the last words of Jules Renard's Journal. I think one needs to read the whole Journal, and have lived with it, to feel this last entry not simply pathetic, but sad, solitary, terrible.

*

Today when I was in the village someone walking behind me began to whistle the air of a hymn, one little known. I recognised it. Turning, I saw a middle-aged farm labourer. If he had been young I should have been astonished. Mine is the last generation brought up to know a great many hymns. And the last which remembers, as a thing felt, the Victorian certainties, hollow as these were, wormed inside, in 1900. Isolated, sarcastically indifferent to the rest of England, our Victorianism was almost of 1840. I rebelled against it, but it had formed and deformed me ; even my revolt was filial. My deepest self, when I am conscious—you won't expect me to answer for any sleeping or disinterested self — is patient, stubborn, a little cracked in its dislike of being told what to do. Anything which is repeated a great many times, a chair, a sentiment, words, repels it. It has no respect at all for its neighbour's opinion. The only thing I have added of my own to this outwardly sober eccentric is the horror of cruelty which disorders my thinking. Not that I am kind — an illusion identifies kindness and dislike of cruelty.

*

12 May. Today, in the train to London, four young soldiers talked to each other in Welsh, and sang — Welsh songs first ; then (I thought it had disappeared with the last war) *Après la guerre fini*. And then, singing softly in parts, so that they sounded like laments, foolish songs in English — even of the last war. . . .

> *I said goodbye to the flowers,*
> *I said goodbye to the trees,*
> *And the little church so quiet,*
> *I said goodbye on my knees. . . .*

Tears came into my eyes without my knowing how they came there ; I stared out of the window to keep them from falling.

The truth is, my despair is so unmanageable that I can let myself cry only over the last war. This one is an agony, always present, and tears are not decent. The cruelty, the young deaths, the abyss of pain, weigh too much ; it insults them to place in the other balance a single grief. And yet I cannot make myself say, with the pacifists : Submit — to the justice of the Nazis. Too many people in Europe have learned to translate the German word for justice into their own words for torture, the closing of schools, hunger, death. My mind hides a rock — it may only be a rock of ignorance or want of vision, but all my thoughts run against it. What — once Hitler had been allowed to grow to great strength and was using it to create an empire which in the moment he chose would compel all other countries to submit — could we have done if we had not fought ? If one could believe that after a long time — how long ? — the elements of good sense in his New Order would neutralise the cruelty and racial nonsense on which it is built, there would be a case for choosing the risks of such a peace to the risks of such a war. My rock is that I cannot believe it, nor find any evidence, material, moral, psychological, for believing. There are things I can believe without evidence — if these match a colour in my mind. But of what colour spread by the Germans in Poland, in Norway, in France, can one believe that it resembles the colour of youth and the colour of joy ? I see us caught — by our own blindness and failures in 1919–39 — in this trap which closes on children as well as on young men, and forced to go on suffering and inflicting suffering until we or the Nazi State are exhausted. And — the real horror — although I write boldly and as carefully as I can about what ought to be done after the war to restore a trembling and ravaged world, I am almost without hope. If I must believe without evidence, I'll believe that our exhaustion will be less than our anxiety to rebuild. Even that is easier than to believe that Messieurs les Grands Intérêts will be defeated in their wish to rebuild a world fit for great interests. How we shall need a force of disinterested intelligence and humanity ! — and where, under the ruins, or in the war graves, shall we look for it ?

But I have no right, in talking or writing, to share my ruinous despair with others. Especially not with young people. . . .

Today in the city there was still the acrid smell of burning, and the clatter of broken glass. Ambulances and police waited outside crashed houses where men have been digging hard for thirty-six hours. A thick fine grit covered the pavements. The air was full of the filthy dust of old houses and fragments of burned paper. There were streets which had given up everything ; they had not kept even a semblance of life. Yet it was here precisely that life clung with the most agonised strength — as though things used by human beings absorb some of their memories and cannot simply be pulverised and scattered. A dark oblong on a fragment of wall kept the shape of a bed or a mirror, and where you would least expect it a cup rested unharmed, between two heaps of rubble. As for the human beings themselves, those whose poor bodies, deformed by their death, had been carried away or were still waiting, under vast piles of stone, the very suddenness with which they had been shocked out of life kept them here. You saw a shadow caress the corner of a wall where there should have been a child's bed, and another pause as though seeking a reflection in a glass, then, turning in the door not there, hesitate and look up, not yet accustomed to seeing the daylight where there should be a ceiling.

These weeks have made our moments fit exactly into moments lived first in China, in Spain. The shrunken spaces between peoples, crossed by a fine web of voices and the steel shuttles, are negligible, almost nothing. Time is the absolute division. Nothing changed in our lives when we were told about the air-raids in Spain ; even Poles, even the thousands killed in Rotterdam in an afternoon, died, for all we felt to the contrary, in the year of the Great Plague. All these events, our own future, became for us, in the very moment they happened, the weak reflection in us of history. It is only now, when the smoke of our ruins joins the cloud above theirs, and our dead are confounded with a vague crowd coming from many countries and all now speaking a common language, that we keep the same time as Chinese, Poles, and the others. In their cities and villages the Americans are not yet our contemporaries.

Our contemporaries are Bede, spending himself to write down the sum of European knowledge in the almost total darkness of the seventh century, Alcuin — who persuaded the Frankish barbarian to admire learning — Dante, Montaigne, Vigny. . . . I know that despair is a sin. Moreover, a sin one must be ashamed of. I suppose that the true intellectual can — to escape this sin of despair, or the odious folly of despising men as hopelessly stupid because they let themselves be trained like cocks to kill each other — offer himself the thought of a great genius, who need only live and his life justifies the nullity and the disappointments of all the others. I prefer to offer myself, offering of which none of us is worthy, the eyes of a young airman, or the eyes, full of kindness and patience, unasking, of an old workman.

*

16 September. Last week was our Congress — of the English P.E.N. By holding it in war-time we avoided the embarrassment and disgrace of having to explain to our foreign writers why it was not opened by the Prime Minister, why no garden-party given by the Secretary for Foreign Affairs, no special performance at Covent Garden of an English opera, no Guildhall banquet, etc. etc. — events which added themselves naturally to Congresses in Warsaw, Prague, and other capitals. It may have — we hope it has — escaped them that in this country the disrespect paid to literature goes so far that writers are perfectly free. We did our best for them. We invited to a luncheon every Ambassador except one, technically neutral, whom none of us could regard as neutral or bearable. . . . I shook hands with Ambassadors, I made speeches prepared and delivered in anguish of mind. Amiable foreigners addressed me as Mme la Présidente. . . . Good. When I came home at the end of the week I found that our servants had left, to go into a war factory. Useless to think of finding others in this village — which in any case we must leave, I to live in London, my sister for a smaller house near her husband's factory. Our lives are coming to pieces in our hands. This house — we took it so that the children could live in the country — is Victorian in its demands, and today Mme la Présidente's back aches and her knees tremble from a day's hard washing and ironing. I iron very badly, I always did. It seems that with an iron energy and good intentions are not enough. A pity. I have enough of both.

During the Congress I had a supreme piece of luck. How, since June of last year, I have combed the London bookshops for Giraudoux I gave away or lent in the illusion that I had only to cross the Channel to buy others — the Channel, which is now a good century wide. Last week I found in Foyle's a soiled shabby copy of La France Sentimentale, uncut. Imagine that its imbecile of an owner let it out of his hands without reading it ! If he has died since, how he must be cursing himself for the folly which has deprived him of so many phrases joining a thing to its opposite, a magpie and Phèdre, despair and a good omelette, life and the night, the cold. I walked off with it in the blazing heat, exalted. If I could have a new Giraudoux, of a good vintage, every month, what a long otherwise dull life I could live happily.

To be able to shut the door of one's room and cut the pages of a Giraudoux consoles for all but the great tragedies (and on how many of these can a journeyman writer count ?) — consoles for disappointments, disillusions, snubs, for a casual infidelity, for failure. Could he sustain one through a real loss ? I doubt it. But why ask of a writer to take the place of courage or a faith ? That is not what they are here for.

Notice that when Giraudoux writes about what is tragic ; war, the disappointments of children, death — you will be surprised when you add up the number of times he concerns himself with nothing smaller — he does it by setting gently in the place of the terrifying image one which is only smiling or innocent. The bitterness, the terror, are penetrated by a light which dissolves them into a rain of bright drops. He is not invariably successful. In moments when his touch fails, the rain is seen to be stage rain, thrown down by a maladroit arm appearing through the canvas. But when he is inspired, when the hive of French poetry, nourished in Greece and (in defiance of French critics of all centuries) in the Italy of Virgil, Cicero, Terence, comes round him and he has only to dip his fingers in the honey, there is nothing, no subject, he fails to turn to a pure joy. He shrinks from none — the cruellest, the most terrible. And to be confronted by them in his words is only a delight. It is not that he lacks the necessary cruelty of writers. It is that he has, very often, the Midas-touch of the poet, and the words given to him turn what is terrible into what is graceful and enchanting, or equivocal. At his worst, into what is arid and glittering, but not, but never, painful.

I refuse to read any book in which the cruelty of the theme gives me more pain than the way it is written impresses and gives pleasure. I am certain that such books are only bad.

*

27 October. How I detest flats, and — depth of vexation — a flat in London, in Portland Place, near Oxford Street, near the B.B.C., near all the plagues of a civilisation dominated by noise and things. When I go out I pass a head porter who looks at me with more than the disdain of porters for a new tenant — he will find that my moroseness is proof against his contempt. True, there is Regent's Park, with its chestnuts and barrage balloon. And from the windows of my room, a curve of modestly small houses which have all the air of houses lived in by human beings, and trees closing the gap at the end — almost a Utrillo. But they are the houses of a mews become — of course — garages, and at midnight and one o'clock a car arrives, with a roar of engines. Doors bang, a self-satisfied voice drawls its orders for the morning, footsteps, the grinding of garage shutters : my heart beats furiously with annoyance ; no air comes in the open windows and I gasp for breath. As soon as I fall asleep it is time to get up.

I am determined to be ill, and it does not surprise me in the least that my fainting fits turn out to be due to an over-strained heart. Not that I believe it — most doctors are fools — but it is as good an explanation as any of my dislike of London.

Yesterday my father sent me a shoe-box full of roses and late white pinks. They had been picked with the shortest possible stems and when they were over-grown — he is so much attached to his ill-kept garden that it needs an effort to send away its flowers. Yet he likes to show he has succeeded in growing them. The piece of paper said : All well October 25th '41. All well — that is what he used to cable from foreign ports, but in a code of which one word stood for : Arrived all well. . . . It seems to me that the roses have a taste of salt on the discoloured petals.

Oh, if I could go home.

I have had a letter from him enclosing a telegram, addressed to me there, from Koubychev — one of those telegrams the Soviet writers send now and then to the English allies they so much mistrust. Who knows what counter-revolutionary adverb I shall insert — innocently — in my reply ?

" . . . I did not know you were communicating with those Roossians — (my father spells as he pleases) — you should watch them, very tricky fellows, Roossians. I have two bowls of roses on the table and more coming out in the garden, I could not get any seeds of Virginia Stock they are pretty little flowers of all colours they make the garden look gay, as soon as one lot dies you drop in more seed and have another show but I could not get any this year, they are using the ground for food. So they say. The days are fine, with bright sun and a light cool wind. We had Germans over last night, the first for a long time. Gooseberries are very scarce and I have not been able to get any. There is no news but I am well and I get plenty of the finest sea and moor air. A pity you cannot. My grandmother's remedy for her weak heart was one teaspoonful of rum in a cup of milk at night and I remember her at eighty-seven as lively as a chicken. I wish you were here, you would see the garden. . . ."

And my aunt. " They have put some big and very powerful Guns over on the east cliff, below the Church, exactly opposite this house. I don't know which suffers more, the windows or my nerves. And last night they began firing, it's unbelievable, just after midnight. The Syren went off at midnight, we heard the German planes going over, and then to everyone's horror those awful Guns started. Naturally people thought it was a Bombardment or something serious, and today there is general indignation and the whole Town protesting at Guns being allowed to go off between midnight and one in the morning. It is no use protesting, the Military will do as they like, but I feel strongly that Gun-practice should be carried out at a more suitable hour. . . . I saw your Parent yesterday, I think he only lives to *contradict*. He put me dreadfully out of patience. . . ." Speaking of an old friend — no, an acquaintance of forty years, scarcely long enough to have relaxed into friendship. . . . " She is ill and I am sorry to say won't get better. I'm truly sorry for her ; I can't but think the War has something to do with it, she has simply let it get the better of her, and is of a most melancholy temperament. You can imagine what she is like now, when she knows she is passing over. I cannot understand Christians behaving like this, after all Death is only going home, and what *welcomes and greetings* we shall have from those who are expecting us ; I'm looking forward to it tremendously. . . . I wonder what you think of the War now. I am hoping against hope that the Russians will hold on and be Victorious ; I shall be terribly grieved if they don't give the Germans a good thrashing, I really think I care more about them than I do about ourselves. We have cut a sorry figure this year, nothing but promises, empty promises. A man said to me yesterday, ' I'm very disappointed indeed with England since the War started.' I replied, ' I'm <u>more</u> than disappointed.' And oh how vexing I find this adulation of the Prime Minister. He may be all they say — but you can believe me, no good will come of letting him think he is infallible. And I would say the same if he were a Minister of the Gospel. At this gait, he'll soon be little better than a *Pope*. . . . Don't you detest Tea without sugar ? But I smile when I think of you as a child, refusing sugar because someone had said you needed sweetening. And you were exceedingly fond of it. . . ."

*

At home.

Everywhere barbed wire, soldiers, army lorries, more soldiers. The two large hotels, and the houses on the cliff — in summer they are let to visitors and the landlady lives in the basement and looks after them ; she goes on living there in the winter, to save money and for warmth — are given up to soldiers. The paint is wearing off, they are terribly shabby, and the little gardens have been trampled to death by army boots. The whole town has grown shabby, as though, with no visitors coming, it would be foolish to keep up appearances.

Our house, although no one is living in it except my father, has become like the others. In all the rooms, dust, cobwebs, discoloured walls. Even in hers. In the early morning the scent of chrysanthemums came into the house, from the few in the garden. I can't stay here, I thought. But I stayed, and in the afternoon I walked through the old town, looking at the restless sparkling water of the harbour. It was a clear day, sunshine, a strong wind, the sky very blue and filled with white clouds the wind could not reach. When I climbed the hill to the cemetery and looked back, the sea was leaning against the sky, the cliffs on either side of the harbour its flying buttresses.

On her grave the southernwood is overgrown ; it needs to be cut back : she would be very vexed. Don't think of your spoiled house, I said to her ; don't think of your bad children. I was ashamed to cry — shouldn't I be crying for myself ? — and I went away and sat on a bench where I could see cliffs, harbour, sea, the Parish Church of St. Mary, all she liked looking at. Why do our memories outlive us and cloud for the living even the bluest sea ?

During the night a few bombs — there had been no warning — fell close to the house. Shocked awake, I lay listening for the next act ; after a minute the door of my father's room opened quietly and he went upstairs to the top of the house, then down to the ground floor, walking as he does always, so softly that he was nearly inaudible. Should I get up and speak to him ? There were no more bombs, and the guns — no doubt thinking of my aunt — had not fired. The old man — he is eighty-seven — padding about in the darkness and silence of his house was part of a solitude in which I have no part. Had he been a stranger I might have felt that I ought to call out to him. Nothing moved me to make a sign. I listened. After a time, I heard the stairs creak, then a board on the landing. His door closed again softly.

The bombs destroyed a house on the cliff near us and some army lorries ; and killed a young sentry. When I saw my aunt she said that with her old servant she had hurried as usual to the basement coal-house. As soon as they were there, seated side by side on chairs placed in the dark entry, the old servant said indignantly, " To think they could go on like this, with Miss Hervey here ! " That I call the finest feudal spirit.

*

1942

When his wife died, a new life, one you can call happy, began for the old sea-captain. At his age happiness is content to fill trivial objects . . . which no one else wants. . . . For the first time, when he was eighty-two, he began to be master — as he used to be master in his ship — in his own house. He had been on bad, that is, on no terms with his wife for many years. Her death — breaking through the walls between them — shocked him. He remembered that they had been young : he saw her, slight, elegant, turn as she stepped down the gang-way from the ship to the quay to look with her young defensive hauteur towards the foreign city ; he saw — only for a moment, since the waking eye has no power over the past — her look of a rebellious boy. It was less these scarcely seen images than the long wave of the past breaking on him, stinging his eyes and forcing the salt between his lips. All the voyages they had made together, the days, the nights, all the harbours, were there, suddenly, together, grieving him. A sharp salt. He stood at the foot of the stairs and wept. His eldest daughter spoke to him with false awkward pity. He repulsed her. She knows nothing, he thought, nothing. Who, now, knew that girl ?

He passed easily, from this confused deep regret, to the little excitements of a death in the house. As if it were the days before Christmas, he went out and bought special fruit to give his daughters. His tears had been shaken from his past, and after the funeral he had no more. Not that the past left him. But it became again his own life, the cloud, full of foreign countries and deceits, he lived in. After a day or two he realised that he was going to be left alone in the house, with an elderly woman coming in daily to clean and cook. He felt a pang, brief, of desolation. But scarcely admitted it, since it would be to admit that he was not loved. Little love as he had given anyone in his life — but where in that hard country could he have found it ? — he was terribly ashamed of slights.

When he was turning over his treasures these days — he had drawers and cupboards filled with what his wife said was rubbish — he found a painting on silk made by a Japanese artist from a photograph of three of his children, the boy and two girls, when they were very young : the boy was still in petti-coats. He gave it to his eldest daughter.

"You're all going, it's no use my keeping this," he said hurriedly.

Like him a moral coward, she chose not to look at the abyss under the words. In that, too, like him. And what, when he spoke, had happened ? Nothing. . . .

Eighty-two. . . . He had left the sea twelve years since, to live at home, always at home. For the first time. What did he expect of it ? What — when he said to himself, Time I stayed at home — had he seen ? Surely not the curious beleaguered life he began almost at once ? . . . Not quite at once. For a few weeks — or months, was it ? — he moved uneasily about the house. During the day he went out, met and talked with other old sea-captains who had laid themselves up in this small port. There were many points of the globe where their memories lay alongside his ; he thought them dull fellows, and most of them mistook the flights of his mind for lies. But he could talk to them and to others ; the morose silence he kept at home vanished, and he was amiable and very friendly, or he con-tradicted. In the evening he sat fidgeting in his wife's sitting-room, vexing her as roughly by his few words as his yawns ; then it was time to shut himself in the kitchen to smoke the strong American tobacco she hated ; then, going up to bed, he paused outside her door to say, "Good-night," and waited until her voice, indifferent, repeated, "Good-night."

He took on himself a few duties, he went to the old market

for vegetables, he gardened. In a short time, between ignorance and his stubborn claim to know, he had destroyed part of the garden. He went on working and planting. Some things grew. It became his garden, and each bud a victory of his will over injustice and neglect. After a longer time, they became kind and friendly and he trusted them.

He gave up entering the sitting-rooms. He lived between his bedroom, at the top of the house, and a room on the ground floor, leading to the garden, which began to be thought of as his, and no one else sat in it. It was in his bedroom he felt safe. Here, at a shabby desk in the window, he cut pictures out of newspapers and magazines. In drawers which he kept carefully locked — even, when he suspected that one of them had been opened, fastened by screws driven through the wood — were all the things he valued. No one knew what he had in them. Now and then he took something from one of the other rooms — a Japanese book he had brought home thirty years earlier, a carved stick — and locked it away. He had a habit, too, of taking things to his room to examine them. If his wife or daughters complained too loudly that they had lost, perhaps a glove, he never returned it. Nothing said, it reappeared one day in full view. Or his grandchild's toys vanished and came back broken. He was very clumsy. Things broke in his hands when he only touched them.

" He is as mischievous as a monkey," his wife said, with bitterness.

But it was not mischief. It was solitude, enmity, fear. As he passed between the outer world, hostile for all it was familiar and common, the streets and harbour of his childhood, and his room, he put his hand out and seized an object. It might — why not ? — turn out to be the answer to a question he never asked : Why am I not loved ? And, too, he was madly inquisitive. His curiosity kept alive in him a child — a being quite other, even in its curiosity, than a monkey. This poor child — what must it have thought of the lies, malice, disappointment, in which he made it live ? So little contents a child that it was often happy.

After all, how little difference there was between an old

captain's beleaguered life in his house and his life during a voyage. No one in the ship advises or interferes with her captain ; he is left alone. Yes, there was a difference, a great one. In his ship he had authority, and the respect, at least of caste. In his house no one respected him.

He made himself, and for twelve years he lived, this stealthy life inside the house, inside the life of the house, which centred wholly on his wife. During these years she turned away from him more and more. At last she could not endure even to eat with him. There were days when she passed him on the stairs without speaking, without a look. He felt, but again without admitting it, cold coming to him from her. The cold of her long disappointment. He rushed away from it. So used now to his stealthy life that he scarcely felt anxious, his mind took refuge in the maze of twisting corridors — dark — even he could not tell lies from truth here. Long since, in this burrow, he had lost himself.

He had no part in the life of his house. Their children belonged only to his wife. And the truth is that he had never been interested in them ; had it been left to him they would have fared badly in all ways. He forgot their names and called any of them by the name of the eldest, the only one for whom he had a little warmth — and she could recall a younger captain, indistinct, who sang *The Two Obadiahs*. But he prepared carefully his Christmas presents, as though all the twenty-fifths of December he had spent at sea were unappeased ; or the rest of tenderness in his life ran into this shallow cup at the foot of the year and he offered it, hopefully — and without hope.

In long walks on the moors he turned over the heap of memories like the tangle of wools he used in darning — he darned with exquisite neatness — and a word, a look, a gesture, from near at hand. His mind clouded with self-pity and anger, and fantasies of triumph. One day he would say such words . . . one day all would see what he was . . . one day . . . His eyes, long-sighted, were caught by a flash of wings, and a clear joy filled him in the sky brim-full of clouds, and the field. He could pick tirelessly for hours, primroses, violets, brambles — like a boy. Out here he was free, and slowly, until he turned home, the day itself took the place of his suspicions and dreams.

If he brought home a good haul of ripe brambles, his wife might say, with a little air of praise,

"That's a good basketful."

Then, secretly, he was pleased. And comforted.

Every evening, before he did anything else, he made a note of the day's weather in a large folio diary, the same size and type as the diary he had kept every year at sea. Now he had no incidents of a voyage to record. Only that it had been fine or rained, and the quarter of the wind. He wrote slowly, a clear backward-leaning hand, very clear. His hand, brown and as if polished, had an air of patience. How many million such words it had drawn after it. . . .

When he resigned, the Line had given him, of grace, a pension of three hundred a year. He was seventy, their senior captain, he had been with them for forty of the fifty-seven years he was at sea. Fifty-seven years. "I was apprenticed when I was thirteen," he would say — if anyone were interested — "I went to Newcastle. It was January. There was snow."

Seven years after he retired — in 1932 — he received a letter :

"DEAR CAPTAIN RUSSELL,

"As you know Shipping is in a very very bad condition, and we have had to effect Economies all round. Not only have we all here in the Office had to submit to drastic reductions but reductions in the wages of Masters, Officers, etc. have also had to be made. I feel that in future we cannot continue paying you a Pension as high as £300 a year : — this amount was agreed upon when the cost of living and everything else was at a very high level. We therefore, propose that your Pension should be £250 per annum. Your cheque for this month will be sent at the rate of £300 per annum but next month's payment will be on the reduced basis.

"Naturally I am very sorry to have to suggest this but I think you will realise that I would not have done so had I not felt compelled.

"Yours faithfully . . ."

When he told his wife, she said with contempt, "They are

a rich firm, they pay a dividend on their shares. It's a mean act."

He would not have this. He made excuses for the Line, times were bad, no, no, it was the right thing — "They'll put it back later." He could not let anyone say that the Line was behaving in a mean way. That would make it seem he was not valued, he was a man the Line was willing to treat badly. He was not that fine captain they had admired and trusted more than the others. . . .

Not long after — obviously he was living too long, longer than they expected he would live — his pension was cut again. Quite brutally this time. To a hundred pounds.

Had he ever been so humiliated? He felt stunned. All his fantasies left him at once and he shivered. He hid the letter and thought he was hiding his distress. But he had given it away to his wife by the haste with which he rushed from the house after reading it, forgetting his stick — to walk distractedly from cliff to pier and pier to bridge. How to tell her, tell anyone, what had happened? He saw only glances, like the bars of a cage. His mind stumbled back and forth, looking for a way out. Under his confusion and shame, an acute grief. To have endured at sea so many years, nearly sixty — forty-four years as master — and be put off with less than two pounds a week. All I am worth to them, he thought. And turned swiftly away. Think of something else. Hide it again quickly with excuses. . . . After days, he brought himself to tell his wife. She did not let him know she had guessed. She was sorry for him, and gentle. It really vexed her that he should be made so ashamed. "They've behaved abominably," she said. But he could not bear pity. He turned clumsily from that, too.

"It will only be for a time. They'll put it back. . . ."

Losing patience with him, she cried, "Do you think so? Not they! They're like all rich shipping firms, too mean for words."

"You don't understand," he defended himself. "I know they wouldn't do it unless they were compelled."

"I understand they've had enough of paying you a pension. They grudge it. And in fact they needn't give you a penny, there's no legal obligation."

He felt less uneasy when she spoke in this voice. It vexed him but its harshness was familiar. " We s'll manage," he said, moving his hands.

" Yes, we shall manage," she said coldly, " and it means going without everything. The little you have invested won't take us far."

And when have you gone without ? he thought bitterly. The other captains' wives pinched and saved where you spent all you wanted — on the house, on the children — dancing-classes — one to the university — and all the money from your mother poured out on that other one. . . . It was an old bitterness. He said nothing. At bottom he was afraid of her. He turned and went heavily up to his room. Sitting at his desk, he reckoned on the back of the letter, slowly, how much he dared spend of his poor savings. If he spent all, it would not fill the gap. *She'll* give her mother things, he thought, of his eldest daughter. Little enough they give me, any of them.

*

The wise thing — now that he was alone — would be to sell this house. If the thought of selling it ever came to him he silenced it at once. His life, at eighty-two, was putting out new branches : it needed this space. He expected to live many many years. Did he expect ever to die ? No one had heard him speak of death.

His daughters went away. Next morning he woke up and felt the silence of the empty house like a breath on his cheek. All the rooms in the house — all those he used to creep into when the family went out, and look quickly through drawers and cupboards, seeking what ? — lay open to him. He was quite alone. He got up and dressed quickly, like a tramp (in trousers and a jacket held together by their stains of grease and soil). Padding downstairs, he raked the stove. The elderly woman came, and because he had decided to go to the shops after break-fast he splashed a little water on his face and changed his clothes.

He went from shop to shop, bargaining, and chaffing the assistants. The older ones humoured him, but the young girls turned their backs, scornful. He hurried home to dinner, pleased that he had saved tuppence. Leaving his tea set for him and covered by a cloth, the woman went away. He was alone again until the morning. He could go out, to the moors, the cliff, the pier. On the cliff the other old captains would greet him with reserve, but they would greet him. He could be unpleasant, he was perhaps mad as well as a liar. But he belonged with them to the remote past of small ships and slow endless voyages. Behind their eyes, they saw the same wharves, the world had for them and him the same simplicity, and the odour of foreign cities and distance. "Ha," one of them would say, "Valparaiso——" and it was enough; each saw and felt it.

There were people in the little town, solitary old men, not sea-captains, who believed all he said. And perhaps they were right and the others unjust and wrong. What lies could be stranger than the truth of his life — beginning that snowy morning in 1868, and covering a world? Now gone.

The order of his days fixed, he was never moved to alter it. They were very full days. He had to find time in them for all the joys of the childhood he had skipped. His evenings were given up to these. The sorting of his stamps. The competitions . . . but about now he gave these up — it was not only that so many of them cost sixpence; it was that he never had a success, never. Even he could not delude himself any longer. . . . His notes on the weather. Dearer than them all, his scrap-books. During the first year he worked on them in the kitchen, as usual, spreading them, and his bowl of paste and the scissors, every evening on the large table. And he kept his bedroom on the top floor. Then, the second winter, he moved down to the first floor, into the better of his wife's two bedrooms — she used to move from one to the other in her restless way, always expecting to surprise sleep. At the same time he took over her sitting-room and made room in it for a large dining-table where he spread his scraps, and had his meals set at one end. Now at last he was at ease in his house, as he had been in his ship. A happiness as new and delicate as a convalescence filled his days from waking to lying down to sleep. And new joys. He covered sheets of paper with designs for his garden. None of them could be carried out, but he saw them, when he was at work there, hovering above the disorder of unpruned roses and beds of wild woodruff, ready to settle, and felt a deep secret pride. What a garden it would be ! Every day, too, he put bread out for the birds ; he watched them, with eyes used to watching, and saw that they have all our needs and troubles. There was even a large old sparrow who was superior to the others and needed — naturally — a larger share of the bread.

One summer his eldest daughter stayed with him for a week. It was so short a time that she laid herself out to please him. She went out with him and he presented her to his friends — who knew very well who she was. But it was as if he said : Look — you thought no one cared about me but here is my daughter, the writer, you know ; and she wanted to see me.

He had become terribly shabby. It was not because he was poor. In his wardrobe hung good clothes he had never worn. All his life, even when he was a young captain, he had put off wearing a new uniform — to wear it would spoil it before the great moment . . . the great moment. . . . His wife used to scold him into a degree of decency. Now he did as he pleased, and it pleased him to dress like a tramp.

*

The house, too, decayed. The sea salt in the air rotted the paint, and inside, the rooms began to look as though they were left open to the north-east gales. One day, the silk of a huge four-fold Chinese screen split across, and some of its padded figures against their backgrounds of rice-field, tea-house, mountain rivers, and sea-coast, lost their inside. The old captain's clumsy attempts to mend it caused other rents. He trod soil and the paste from his scraps into the delicate old rugs. The house was too large for one woman to keep clean, but he did not notice that it was neglected and dirty. Then came the war : a bomb blew in several windows at the back of the house ; he had them boarded up, darkening the rooms.

For the rest he ignored the war — except when he wrote angrily to his daughter that " some fools think me too old to manage a ship ". Every disaster of its first years was only a proof of the everlasting superiority of England and the Tory party. It vexed him intolerably when people talked of mistakes. Neither England nor the Tories had ever made a mistake, nor ever would.

When his eldest daughter came again, she was shocked by the desolation of the house. Less than five years since her mother died, and nothing of her lingered in the rooms she had loved as a second self. The old captain — he was eighty-seven — was destroying everywhere. Two panels of the ruined screen, torn from the others, leaned against the wall of his room. Among the disorder of a room shrouded in dust-sheets she found the remains of the Chinese cabinet made of many different woods, where her mother had kept pieces of fine lace. Somehow he had destroyed the lacquer, then broken it off its pedestal. The scent still clung to it — of the past, of voyages.

In some of the rooms the paper hung from the walls, and everywhere were cobwebs and dead leaves — it was autumn, they drifted in and lay about — the colour of his hands. He lived now almost entirely in the rooms which had been her mother's, squatting there in disorder and dust.

He fell ill that winter — the third winter of the war. It was the first serious illness of his life. His housekeeper, a dutiful woman, looked after him and he recovered. He never spoke about his illness. He wanted to forget it and he put down to the cold and the winter roads his curious uncertainty when he went out. He waited for the spring to give back his strength.

Spring overlooked him. It had other things in war-time to do than trouble with an old captain. . . . Summer. His long practice in evasions found him every conceivable excuse — except his feeling of giddiness — for walking far. He talked of going to the moors, he never went. But then a miracle did happen. One day at the end of October he had a letter from the Line beginning : " Owing to the increase in the cost of living — (had they just noticed it ?) — it has been decided to raise the allowance paid to you to £200 per annum. This will commence from the 1st November. . . ."

The joy, the relief he felt, had scarcely anything to do with the difference between two and four pounds a week. Suddenly he wished with an almost painful sharpness that he could hear his wife saying drily, " I see you had a letter from the Office ? "

Holding the letter, he stumbled upstairs, chuntering under his breath. " You see, they put it back. Part of it. I knew they would as soon as they had it. I told you." He stood in the doorway of her room. What was beating in him that was not his heart ? " You see, they can spare it now. . . ."

He wrote his eldest daughter, holding the news back until the end of the letter. To the Line.

" DEAR SIR,

" Your welcome letter to hand, re increase in Pension. I cannot find words to thank you for it, it's like a ray of sunshine in a heavy Atlantic gale, my only regret is that I am not able to do anything to earn it, and every time a Convoy passes I have an intense longing to be at sea again and doing my share in it.

" I am still hoping that I shall have a chance for I have an old score to pay back to the Germans and it's better to die fighting than rusting out.

" I am keeping fit and in good Health and ready for anything that comes along.

" I trust you are well.

" Now I will finish and thanking you again for your Generosity."

*

He died less than a fortnight later. One evening, when he had laid out his scrap-books for the evening's work, he decided first of all to rake the stove in the kitchen. But suddenly the room tilted forward as though in a heavy sea, he fell, burning his hand, then stumbled up and fell, again and again, until he saw it was no use, and lay still. He lay there the long November night. At moments he knew he was lying helpless in a place of pain ; and at others it seemed quite natural to him that he should look down and see, cold in its white light, the snow covering the narrow street by the harbour and the footsteps in it of a young man of thirteen leaving his mother's house to apprentice himself to Captain William Kirby.

In the morning the woman came, and his neighbour's sons carried him upstairs. He lived, as they say, for five days. They told him to expect his eldest daughter : obediently he expected her. When she came he looked at her without interest. With the terrible insight he now had, he knew she did not care for him. A greater warmth came to him from the district nurse and his neighbours. He knew himself, too — at last — and, without glancing at them again, he laid down his rough defences against life. They had never been needed. It had been a mistake, and very gladly he found that his childhood was still waiting for him, in the same cool light, to begin. . . . Close to him he felt someone suffer. The nurse asked loudly and kindly, " Well, captain, how do you feel ? " Each time she asked it, he answered, " I'm all right." It was his last signal, before the distance became too great. . . . He had nothing to do but live the lifetime of gentleness and stoicism he had intended. Each time one of the women bent over him she saw his silence make another effort to finish what it had to say about his happy life. No one ever ended a voyage more simply.

*

His eldest daughter had to arrange for his grave. " Of course you will wish the captain to be buried with his wife . . . ? " She explained calmly but with a secret confusion that that was not possible ; room had been found for her mother in the old Hansyke grave, near *her* mother ; it would never do to lay Captain Russell there. Looking at the clerk as she said all this, she thought : And if you knew how vexed she was when he came into her room for a moment . . . and yet — would she be vexed ? Perhaps now . . . what can I know of their hearts ?

" There must be a Russell grave somewhere," she said smoothly.

The man turned back and back in his folios, guided by dear knows what thread stretched underground. At last he stopped, and with a little surprise showed her the entry made in 1822 — when Nicholas John Russell, mariner, had bought his lot, near the sea-ward boundary. He consulted another folio and said, " That's lucky. There's room for one."

There were still things she had to do. She forced open the drawers in the upper bedroom. They were filled, she found, with the broken rubbish of his voyages, photographs, so many photographs, dried tropical leaves, shells, foreign coins. The photographs, when she was breaking them in pieces, tried to save themselves by becoming memories. They were not hers. Then books of his clear writing, the ink of the first already grey. These were filled with poems he had copied out of newspapers, noting under each not the name of the author but the paper — thus the *Sydney Herald* had the credit of writing *Maud* — and jokes, hundreds of jokes, and drawings, traced and neatly coloured, of women usually in corsets. She filled sacks with the torn pages. And in another room she found wooden sea-chests full of the tall folios — forty-four, as many folios as years — in which since his first voyage as master, in 1881, he had recorded every day the weather and his observations on ports, harbours, cargoes, currents — " Between Cape St. Roque and St. Lucia found equatorial current weak and from that bearing it was frequently hidden by the trees " — foreign cities, with strange personal asides which perhaps had been written for her mother's eye. She was sure that her mother had ignored any chance put in her way to read these millions of words. Yes, millions, many millions. In hour after hour at sea, alone in his cabin, more alone in the rigour of his authority, he wrote on slowly. In port, he wrote down everything, the price of fruit, the names of streets — " They had one of their Revolutions so-called the month before we come and of course new names on the streets to celebrate " — the history of the country, the foreign names of birds, perfumes, a mountain. His mind noticed with the joyful indiscrimination of a child, and a seafarer's patience : it forgot nothing.

They must be destroyed, she thought. She began by tearing the large stiff pages without reading them. But the clearness of his hand-writing was inescapable ; from each book when she opened it some image stepped out, and she could not deny it its moment of life — the last. Each as it came was less and less like the tall shabby old man stumbling about his empty house.

There was the one, senior but not yet the oldest captain, whose ship was sunk by the Germans during the last war. He began writing at once on the German cruiser, in a small notebook squeezed in among the folios as that year in German prison camps was pressed between the others. The entries went on through the year, very brief : the food, his health — he was often ill from the bad food and the entry was simply, " In the Lazarette "; but once when he was in hospital in Charlottenburg he wrote, " When will freedom come ? " It seemed to come in March 1918. He had been sent home with other prisoners of his age — he was sixty-three — and his daughter remembered his arrival and her mother's indifference, and that no one asked him to describe his year, or the sinking. Nevertheless in the small book the entry ran : " Home, the weather clear and cold, light SW–W winds, smiling faces and a warm welcome."

Did he, as he wrote the last words, try to believe them ? Before the end of the war he was back at sea.

There was the collision in the North Sea, at night, in a thick fog, with a Swedish ship his own struck amidships. He took her crew on board " 13 over the bows and 3 by lifeboat ", and shook hands with each man as he stepped on the deck, affably, as if it were a social occasion, while he noticed that one and all were carrying luggage, and reflected that there was something odd about the whole business. He retired to his cabin and under the eyes of the Swedish master covered pages with his suspicions. . . . " This after 30 years master without an accident, and to run down an old ship that look as if she was wilfully put athwart of a busy track for someone to hit. I cannot imagine a master of a steamer stopping her and letting her lie athwart of a track where he must have known that all steamers between Huntcliff and Flambro are steering on a course in a line with the shore whereas if he wished to remain stopped in a dense fog why he did not steam farther off the Land clear of shipping. . . . The ship being 36 years old was better lost than saved."

At the end of the years he filled the pages headed Memoranda with soliloquies his daughter suspected had been meant for his wife's eyes. In that clear pale glass these naïve untruths would have reflected only images of derision. The last day of the year was the anniversary of his wedding — (under that date, 31 December 1883, the entry was : " Light breeze and dull throughout. Married this morning at the Parish Church at 8/am and proceeded from there to Liverpool "). He never failed to find words so insincere that they were pitiful — written in the trustful conviction that he was telling the truth, and for a woman who never existed. Even the very young girl he married, with her eager temper, her vitality, was not gentle enough to forgive him for his habit of lying. She was too scornfully direct to ask herself why a man brave and accurate in his dealings with the sea lost and betrayed himself so clumsily with human beings — she among them. " He vexes me beyond bearing with his lies," she used to say, the anger in her voice terrifying her children.

He must sometimes have vexed himself. The last pages of 1907 were bare except for two sentences.

" Nothing to remember but faults.

" Distance run from Sandy Hook to Monte Video 5747 miles, time steaming *32* days *22* hours, average speed 7.28 Knots : anyone wishing to see the record of this remarkable quick passage can do so at the Office ; yet some people are so envious they will not acknowledge that my ship can move."

*

The hand tracing the lines, line after line, every day, the days becoming years, the tall captain becoming a weather-worn eccentric old man, stopped. Surely, my God, of all this lifetime of effort, one word could have been saved ? Why not this, written in Bahia : " So ends the year 1896 under a clear sky and in Tropical Waters miles from home " ?

His eldest daughter recalled that in turning out a drawer she had found his two war medals, which no one when he was alive remembered he had. She fetched them and pinned them on his jacket between the folds of white, ridiculous and decent, covering him. She asked him to forgive her for destroying his life's work. Tears sprang to her eyes, really of pity for him. A pure pity, since his absence meant nothing. But who, when his life, mutely going off after enduring hard things so long, turned and laid down its great store of unshared memories, would not have wept for it ?

And in fact, she had always felt a queer sympathy for him. The aversion she learned young, from her mother, did not succeed in killing it, only drove it shamefully to hide itself. My mind, she thought, is as tortuous as his. We are alike. No one else will cry over him. . . . Then she felt sure that her mother, if she had lived, would have cried. But for whom ?

*

It surprised her — as when she was praised herself — to find that many persons in the town, small and guarded as it was, respected him. He was a character, they said, and so few are left.

And it is true that in any part of the modern world there are now only a few characters. Most of us have long ceased to have opinions and feelings of our own or to take that unhurried interest in living which is necessary if we are to be anything more than a set of gestures, useful in letting other people know in which pigeon-hole of society we belong. But, she wanted to ask them, what character ? Are you thinking of the faithful experienced captain, with his habit of courage ? Yet this was the very one who found spiteful ways of punishing an officer he disliked. And when his young son sailed with him, he bullied the boy, who was anxious to do well and very brave, so mercilessly that he ended the voyage desperate and nervous. If she had shown any weakness, he would have bullied his wife. When, during the war, the boy, and soon after his seventeenth birthday, earned a Médaille Militaire and a little later the M.C., he felt only a sour envy and told him, " Others have done more and had nothing." To see the boy's five medals — he was killed — set out in the case in his wife's room angered him. Where are my two ? he thought bitterly. Not once, not by one word, did he praise the boy to his wife or speak a sorrowful word when he was killed.

But what is the use of placing side by side, like algebraic signs, the queerness nourished in long slow voyages, in the loneliness forced on the master of a ship, his wish to be shabby, the instinctive lies, his fear of disapproval, the endless patience, his deep bitter resentment, flowing down through all the veins of his life, of his wife's contempt for him, his unwilling submission to the will in her delicate body, his shame, never acknowledged, of the harm he did her in marrying her ? Everything is missing from the equation — even if one had the rest of the terms. Even if room were found for the child of thirteen stooping, in the room in Newcastle — there was a stove and engravings of ships — to write his name at the foot of the parchment headed Ordinary Apprentice's Indenture.

A very strange thing — in those days his writing sloped as far forward as that in the forty-odd folios leans back. When did he begin retreating from life ?

Leaning forward eagerly, the child enters his life, " voluntarily binds himself " ; and promises that for the term of five years he " will faithfully serve his said Master, his Executors and Assigns, and obey his and their lawful commands, and keep his and their secrets . . . and will not do any damage to his said Master, nor will he consent to any damage being done by others, but will, if possible, prevent the same ; and will not embezzle or waste the Goods of his Master . . . nor frequent Taverns or Alehouses, unless upon his or their business ; nor play at Unlawful Games : IN CONSIDERATION WHEREOF, the said Master " will teach him the business of a Seaman, and pay him £40 during the five years, beginning the first year with six, " the said Apprentice providing for himself all sea-bedding, wearing apparel, and necessaries. . . ." He lays the pen down, with that already doubtful smile. The Marine Superintendent shakes hands with him, with that condescension of the knowing adult for the open and defenceless. He opens the door for his secure decent Master, follows him out, and is never seen again.

A character. Its bitter must, clouding the whole, was surely formed then. From the cold of that first winter, the bleeding rawness of his hands while they were losing what childishness they brought with them, hardness, cruelty, the coarse thumbs pressing him into shape, the brief cheap gaieties, the clouded eyes staring at the foreign streets and the hand seeking in the pocket a few pence. He told no one. Who would have seen anything in so common a tale ? Even he only remembered clearly, and sometimes spoke of it, the snow lying everywhere that day.

*

What a pleasant place Nicholas Russell chose! At this height, and on this side, nothing came between it and the finest of views. You looked towards the east cliff, balancing its Church and the broken Abbey, to the sea, and down on the tranquil harbour with its plumed houses — there is always smoke tarnishing, softly, the air over the roofs. Except for the family, the mourners were very old men, on duty : an old sea-captain, and a retired pilot, so old that their life was all on the surface, the lightest breeze would have dissipated it.

The eldest daughter kept her gaze on the sea. A clear cold day, without wind, she said to herself, and thought : I'm getting the habit, but I'm not good at it yet : I should know which quarter this no-wind is coming from. . . . She saw the old captain walking, his tall body leaning forward a little in its dreadful clothes, towards the town. Oh, poor soul.

For what, this long life, oh for what ? To the eldest daughter at this moment, it seemed that she had been left an undecipherable scroll of memories of ports, voyages, skies, seas, dangers — all that the old captain had carried with him so long, and for what, for what ? Walking through the ancient streets, with their secretive alleys and flights of worn steps, their restless glimpses of water, a mooring-post, a sunk wharf, a gull, she looked in them for the answer. In all these narrow streets, but never both of them at one time, she saw — if you can call seeing what is no clearer than the reflection of water in sunlight — the captain and the captain's wife. Guard them carefully, she cried to the flagstones, to the walls eaten by the salt : guard them for me when I can no longer.

It did not seem to her impossible that, hurrying towards the bridge, or the cliff, the captain's wife would one day come face to face with a girl. But it would need, surely, his longest voyage for the old captain to come up with his still trusting look. He learned distrust young. And yet — so patient a curiosity, and lasting his life, could it belong to anyone but a child ?

*

A young man of this war has complained that the survivors of the last, now in their forties or fifties, cannot understand his anger at being driven into the boredom and danger of a war. Why does he think that they have lost their memory ? Because they survive ?

He complains, too, that the young men of that war were so ignorant they enjoyed it. I am tempted to be foolishly angry or laugh. Too many young men live in my memory, and only there — phantoms who at moments remember their fresh looks : one of them, the youngest, remembers his stammer, another his wish to finish writing a poem, another his little joke about leave trains : I have forgotten it but I recall that Victoria station which was a part of our bodies where a nerve had been rubbed bare : another remembers his fear of losing an arm, and another that he had never eaten as many strawberries as he wanted. The young writer of this war says they were careless, and not bored. . . . He is lying.

No, he is only dull. He does not see what shadow crosses his. Of the young men he is talking about, I saw a few during their last leave — and I know what they were thinking. They thought, with regret, with love, that there were things they would have done if they had had time, that books are made to be read, bodies to be touched, countries to be visited, and they regretted the little they had read, touched, seen. And they thought the war terribly boring and uncomfortable.

Does it matter ? Not to the young men who have settled themselves so easily in the grass of France. To the young scolding soldier of this war, then ? A little. Since if you are insensible it is no use, even supposing you are not killed, hoping to write what, when they read it, will change people's lives.

*

The parlour of a small French house is too full of things arranged for the absence of human beings. They would gladly, the two Englishmen, move half of them to the attic, but it is impossible, they are not allowed to change anything. They can open the window. They do, and the clear warmth of June in France, clear, even in northern France, of any under-current of cold, filters into the room the sky, bees, and a sensation of arms stretched like the horizon. Young, very young, their khaki blurs muscle and quickness without spoiling them. Smith, slightly the elder, is also the one who more easily balances his senses with his will. He speaks as the young often do, half to himself.

Smith.—How many of them are there, carts, lorries, bicycles, cars with mattresses, without mattresses, children, a sewing-machine, a parrot, the hunchback? When I saw them first coming along the road I thought : Always the same paraphernalia, refugees never learn a new trick. Then they began practising their new trick, rolling into ditches, their bodies split open on the road, throwing themselves across the children — why? It wasn't until I caught the look on a woman's face and remembered my own eyelids stretching like that, my skin stiffening across my cheeks to form a mask, that I saw what she was seeing, yes, I saw the planes — and the plane shooting us up on a road near Givenchy. So they use them on refugees now. . . .

Johnson.—Always the same friendly Boche.

Turning, Smith jerks his head at the sofa where a third person, an English soldier a little older than either of them, but young, is sleeping, a hand under his round cheek.

Smith.—Do you think he's really dead?

Johnson.—Oh, I think so. He's very quiet.

Smith.—So was that other. That one I watched for an hour, hours, until suddenly he began to talk to himself about a field of long grass, and to stroke it. I almost began to feel it under my own hands, the lightness, the dew chilling my fingers, the rough sharpness of a blade. Then I was at home, over my knees in a meadow blazing with marguerites and delicious with quaking-grass ; and then I was sitting with my father, I saw the braid on his sleeve, he was, you know, the captain of a tramp steamer, beside the disused ramparts in Antwerp : my finger was bleeding, I had cut it on a reed in the ditch. You know how it is with us now : seized by a memory, we're changed into it, it takes possession, nothing prevents it from flowing through all the veins of our bodies. . . . When I came back to myself — a few minutes, days, was it, later ? — he had gone. The thing I really regret was the book I caught sight of in his pocket. He could have told me what people like us are writing now. Like that Frenchman the other day who brought us Valéry and Charles Péguy.

Johnson.—Ever since I've been hoping to find his Péguy. No luck — he must have contented himself with a part of France I don't know.

Smith.—*Dans le recourbement de notre blonde Loire*, no doubt. . . The other is still alive. He enjoys as much as he ought to the miracles of living, the light, the salt wind, yet he knows more about us than we know of ourselves. I should be glad to hear from him where he learned it. . . .

It is only after he has been talking for a minute that he realises he is alone ; Johnson has gone. But the other young man stretches himself on the uncomfortable sofa, yawns, and sits up. At once he looks at Smith with the air, defensive and friendly, of a child waking in a strange room. He speaks first, with a timidly friendly smile.

Green.—Good-morning, my name's Green. Did you bring me in ? Decent of you.

Smith.—Where were you ?

Green.—Lying out in a field near the road. I heard the shell. . . .

Smith.—Have you seen this house before ?

Green.—Oh, yes. I slept in it a week, or two weeks was it ? since.

Smith.—Are you sure ?

Green *laughs.*—This or one very like it.

Smith.—One like it. . . . Now you're here, tell me — what have you brought ? A book ? Poems ? Good — I used to read poetry. I even wrote — badly . . . but talk, tell me everything you know.

Green.—Do I know anything ? Why, yes — yes — what a hive. . . . Stop ! No, I can't stop them, they drone in and out, a swarm of bees. I see them.

Smith.—Close your eyes.

Green.—I still see them. . . .

Smith, *quietly, almost with love.*—You wouldn't see them if
you weren't dead. Nor this room — which is so like the one
you slept in. You would see a field, they must have made a
field where the house I know stands. It was here in 1914. You
won't stay here long, it's not one of your real memories. But
you have time, you have the whole of time now — for everything
but the things you had no time to enjoy before you were killed.
Don't go without showing me . . . whatever you are carrying
with you, to show us. . . .

Green.—Us ?

Smith.—You talked about us, not very often, when you
were alive. We were your elders, exactly of your age : we
had carelessly got ourselves killed in the last war. How clearly
I can see — any moment I shall begin to think I remember
you. . . . You're not unhappy . . . you smile. . . . See how
easy it is to be dead — and how empty. If one had no hope
of going further . . .

Green.—What can I show you ? What had we ? Our pre-
knowledge of this new war ? The despair we passed off as
scepticism ? We learned it from your friends who were not
killed. But was it despair ? — or just a fashion ? What do you
want to know ? What the sun feels like across the top of a
bare shoulder ? Its shocking brightness on the sea ? The taste
of dark honey ? I'm nearer to them than you.

Smith.—No . . . don't cling to what you must sooner or
later let go. Tell me — since you know — since you remember
so much — more than you knew you knew — who are your
poets ? What did they write between our wars ? Since ? I
remember a few names — but tell me as well about all those I
don't, since they weren't born then, or they were children.
What is the name of our Valéry ?

Green.—Good God, he doesn't exist.

Smith.—Are you going to disappoint me ? At least let me
look, let me see. Let me hear.

Green.—A great many of us wrote poetry : when you believe
you have very little time it seems easier to begin with a few
verses. With luck they will be finished. And our elders —
Spender, Day Lewis, Auden——

Smith.—Foolish of me, but I expected to hear other names. . . .
But go on, go on. I had no time to use up my curiosity,
my impatience. I still have them, I still live out of myself to
the future. Talk — I want new words. Words, phrases, I can
go down into, always deeper—

Presque tombeau vivant dans mes appartements,
Qui respire et sur qui l'éternité s'écoute. . . .

Green.—You expect too much. The writers you know
nothing about are all minor poets — those of them whom without being foolish one can call poets. They began to write
when they were very young, and they echoed two very admirable poets, Hopkins and Eliot. It's right, I think, that we should
do our exercises in that way, and let them be printed and criticised. But they went on writing and writing and publishing :
so anxious they gave themselves no time for that concentrated
and hard mental effort which alone could have helped them to
see themselves, their emotions, their sensations before life, the
relations of all these with whatever in nature is unchanging,
really to see these, not only to have feelings about them and to
turn these into verse with the help of a technique borrowed here
and there and hastily applied. They are fond of quoting a passage
from a German poet, dead now, whose rhythms, when these had
been transposed into English and altered, they imitated : *Verses
are not, as people imagine, simply feelings (these we have soon enough) :
they are experiences.* But they never understood what this meant.
It would never occur to one of them, as it did to the French
poet you admire so much, to give up a long time, years, to
placing himself in the real world. Perhaps they felt there was
not enough time for that. . . .

Smith.—How I sympathise with them !

Green.—I needn't — being one of them. . . . They never
even examined their thoughts, to see whether these bore any
relation to things-as-they-are. I don't mean they should have
tried harder to write a poetry of ideas. Heaven forbid. They
have, some of them, only too many lame and decrepit ideas.
There was a period when, in lieu of thought, they accepted the
ideas of Marx as interpreted for them by a political party. We
— I mean my friends — ought to be grateful to them for having

this chicken-pox : immunised, we didn't take it. They, too, got over it, but have they thought since ? Scarcely at all. Indignation, confused, or a vague pity for victims, quickly becoming self-pity, in Spender. In Dylan Thomas a self-conscious and simple sexual imagery, at the level of the crudest Catholic symbolism, almost an inversion of those symbols : and to become conscious, unbearably, of their cardboard roughness, you need only place them beside one verse or another of Baudelaire, he haunted by his Catholic heredity and, deeper, by the most primitive of religious terrors——

Smith.—By that aspect of Catholicism which Mallarmé describes as offering *des entrailles à la peur qu'a d'elle-même, autrement que comme conscience humaine, la métaphysique et claustrale éternité.* . . .

Green.—In George Barker, a desperate jigging and pirouetting, mechanical, as if each of his emotions were connected by a wire to its object. Auden. . . . But what use is it for me to give you a great many names — and no new words ? So much of the poetry we wrote was a private titillation. So many of us wrote, write, verses equal in weight and depth to the accounts given of their emotions by well-meaning novelists. We were all slaves to the object, to things. Violently as many of us reacted against it we were part by our nerves and thoughts of the mechanical civilisation we despised. We could neither change objects by assimilating them, nor love them and so create them — which I see now is the motive really of love. We used and arranged and played with objects in our poetry as if they were pieces of a meccano set. We imagined that construction has something to do with this game. Some of us were, as we thought, admirably simple — without a notion that simplicity is the end of a long arduous process, that it cost your Valéry a lifetime to be able to write,

> *Qui pleure*
> *Si proche de moi-même au moment de pleurer ?*

that a succession of our puny and fanciful images contained barely one meaning, not to dream of the strict concentration of many meanings into one image which is truly simplicity — as it is everything else. One of the three writers we thought of for a few years, the later years of *l'entre deux guerres*, as our leader, Auden——

Smith.—You were going to speak of him before, and hesitated. Why?

Green.—Because he mystified me when I was alive, and still does. Of the three he had by far the strongest intellect, his perceptions were always acute, he saw the relations between things wildly dissimilar; his curiosity was, or it seemed to be, limitless; the answers his mind gave to the questions he put to it were always subtler, and he controlled them. Less, far less ignorant of himself than Spender, more inquisitive, more restless, bolder, than Day Lewis, he had finer possibilities than either of them, and his greatest danger seemed — then — the ease with which he moved about among an infinitely greater number of objects and recognised them with clearness and familiarity. Why trouble to explore when you are already richer, in images, in associations, and in the management of these, than any of your friends? He was careless because lazy. He would sometimes throw together in the form of verses symbols which had less energy than the language a child finds to talk to his puppy when he thinks they're not overheard, or a neurotic's habit of touching or avoiding lines. But he excited us, he seemed confident; no line, so far as I remember, he wrote, implied that he should be admired or pitied or even liked. He was disinterested.

Smith.—Well?

Green.—The truth is that I don't know why he left Europe to avoid the war he — like the rest of us — saw coming, I don't know whether to admire in him the resolution he made and carried out, facing what he knew would be disdainful comment from the many, to guard his integrity as a poet from the distraction of war and the worse distractions of hate, fear, grief, all the hardening and limiting a war fastens on us——

Smith.—You have described a man for whom the many are indifferent.

Green.—He may have felt that Europe was doomed. He may have fled, not from the war but from the Dark Age.

Smith.—The man you describe must have known that the Dark Age is darkest for those outside it.

Green.—I daresay. But if I can't admire him — and it's true I can't, nor will he need or expect it — can I regret what seems to me a grievous miscalculation on the part of so ingenious a man? Is it possible that, without injury, he can break himself from his past? Can he establish, between himself and America, the correspondences a poet must have between himself and the outer world, in order to find it again in himself? Where will he draw energy, with so many channels stopped, and by an irrevocable act? His readers, and those of his generation who survive, will learn, in five? twenty? years, whether a poet can not only grow but grow loyally after the refusal, so harsh, so almost brutal, of an experience which seemed made for him. Do you remember Gide? — *Tout ce qui cherche à s'affirmer se nie.* . . . *Ce que tu prétends protéger en toi s'atropie.* Does it apply even to the integrity, the will to be himself, that Auden was anxious, justly, to save? I don't know — but I know, although I hate to admit it, that I was disappointed and deeply wounded when he went away. It seemed to me, and still does, that he was injuring and making little of something we had in common, which was valuable, which we ought to have guarded, with all we had, if it was necessary with our minds and our precious — I mean it seriously — bodies. I can't describe to you what this something is, since it must take a different form for each of us. For me it was the curve of a road I could see from my bedroom window, crossing the side of a hill to a group of trees. Alas. . . .

Smith.—For me it was not one thing, it was several, all of them common and simple.

Green.—A sort of hypocrisy, nervous, a false charity, because aimed obliquely at myself, makes me ashamed to accuse Auden of a betrayal, a want of friendship — oh, not to me. . . .

Smith.—Yes, I know. I had the same experience in 1914, with a close friend. Instead of coming with me, he chose, for the best, the most reasonable of reasons, to find work in a reserved occupation. I was angry when anyone criticised him, and he did, I believe, useful work. . . . I had forgotten him until you spoke. Speak of something else.

Green.—When at last the war came, it put an end to a great deal of intolerable maundering and whimpering. I am ashamed to remember how solemnly we pitied ourselves during the thirties. From our verses I could make a laughable anthology of groans and sighs. Who wrote :

> *Leave, leave the sad star that is about to die.*
> *Laugh, my comedians, who may not laugh again —*
> *Soon, soon,*
> *Soon Jeremiah Job will be walking among men ?*

Who : *We have no home. Our bourgeois home is wrecked ?* Who : *For them everything is drowned by the rising wind, everything is done against time ?* And who :

> *Seeing beyond our noses*
> *A land never to flow with milk and honey,*
> *But winter a stone throw off and no more roses ?*

All these, and many other voices as weak and puerile, run together in my mind in a shallow stream without light. If for an instant I think I am going to seize something in it, it has vanished before I can make it out. Is this one of the effects of dying ? It can't be — others of my memories are only too clear, too dazzling.

Smith.—They can never have been alive, your little Jeremiah Jobs. How they would have bored me. How little I have missed. . . . Only the sun, the seasons, voices, tastes, a child. . . . But go on. And now ? Even poets — who would turn the world upside-down for a phrase — are forced to notice a war. Though not, thank heaven, to let it dictate their verses.

Green.—The two poets we expected most of — two apart from Auden — have changed, certainly. Spender less than the other. He was always a divided writer. In his early poetry, verses not unintelligent, not unshapely, not without charm — one is almost forced to describe it by negative adjectives, by what it is not — were followed, apparently without his noticing the change, by verses stammering a diffuse emotion, phrases unconsciously vulgar or meaningless, confused or flaccid thought, exactly like a man whose involuntary gestures contradict his willed poise or pose. Immediately below the surface even his happiest phrases flew apart, there was so little fusion between idea and object. But if I am not deceiving myself, his latest poems, full like the others of self-pity, are none the less an effort to disinterest himself. He is not yet able to separate his emotions from the objects they offer him, or to reflect a clear image of experiences which have moved him, or relate his experiences to life except on superficial levels. But it seemed to me that the effort had been made, it existed in spite of failure, helpless tumbles into bathos and a conventional imagery — the newest clichés, of course. . . . *Nipples of bullets*. . . . *Enthusiastic scent*. . . . He is tempted, and only sometimes resists, to inflate a trivial or respectable image with a gust of imprecise emotion, so that it wobbles and sways on the point of bursting. Or by confusing a number of symbols — more often, a number of those less significant images which are metaphors — he offers a smudge of his experience. Or of ideas not worth the trouble of elaborating — they could not be compressed, they would disappear — into verse. Or liberal and humane sentiments, irreproachable as opinions, are expressed in a vague flat way or with an emphasis which calls attention to their decent ordinariness. But here and there in these new poems a spontaneous brilliance, a brief certainty of power or knowledge : for the space of a few verses, or a few lines, he is sure of himself, sure of what he has felt or seen, and able to give an account of it in terms of poetry. Here, I thought, when I was reading and re-reading, here perhaps is a poet, if he would wait. If he were not driven, by some anxiety, to show what he can do. His danger is quite different from the danger we imagined for Auden. He has fewer easy certainties, he is not amused by his own wit and mental agility, he would not, I think, say to himself : Why wait when I can write so well now ? Rather it would be : Why wait when I am suffering like this ? people should know how over-sensitised I am, how acutely I feel. And yet it does not seem impossible — or it does not yet seem impossible — that at some moment it may occur to him to give up trying to express his feelings with the greatest sincerity and suggestiveness, and try instead to make them yield the purest and most exact poetry.

As for Day Lewis, he was always the cooler, more apt to regard his sensations and thoughts as objects. He seemed, too, to take a greater and simple pleasure in his impulse to write poetry. He had a gaiety which is very pleasing, and more modest than Auden's self-amusement. His latest poem — and the last I shall read——

Smith.—You will have all the keener pleasure in listening to the rest of them when he brings them with him.

Green.—Perhaps. . . . I am sure at least that his poetry will mature more naturally and gracefully — a good loyal little wine — than the others, that at every stage he will be more firmly in control of his mind's energy. In his latest poem — it is in some sort a meditation on the idea of time as a state of being, a sensation carrying with it its weight of desires and thoughts — the symbols he finds correspond exactly to the sensations and memories he collects in himself. Certainly he has the will to see his own nature and the nature of life clearly, and to express clearly, and with the appropriate subtlety, what he sees. I only wonder whether he has the persistence. . . . Already I begin to see what effort is needed, what relentless labour, *de n'attendre pas la mort pour mourir.*

Smith.—But are there no very remarkable poets living in our country ?

Green.—Certainly there are. I can think of three — Walter de la Mare, T. S. Eliot, and Edith Sitwell. They are all older. The last of these interests me extremely. I have watched her move, from that early dance of all her senses and wit, to a profound sensibility, exquisitely controlled, a suppling of the intellect, to an ease in discerning the relations between things, to an always greater power to concentrate images and sensations within the forms of a poetic statement — if statement were not too frigid a word for these apparitions which are her newest poems. How I regret not being able to read the poems she will write. Her brilliance has a contour, her light obscurity and warmth. To a clear intellect she joins superbly firm senses and a delight in exercising both. Her wit moves between what is most abstract and what is most gentle and touching. It opens an abyss of quietness or horror, descends into it, ascends, always seeking what it never loses, the double note of existence——

Smith.—Which here, if you listen, is single.

Green.—My ears are still burning from those other sounds.

Smith.—You are not sufficiently dead. . . . But don't listen — yet. . . . You know, all these notes — of existence, as you say — have their source here. You'll leave me, to find one of them, to listen to death flowing away into life. And I have so many questions unanswered. Were there no young poets ? All these you have talked about are older than I am.

Green.—Oh, any number. Their verses are both trivial and serious. Serious because they have a foreboding, trivial because they are only poets by default — default of life. Few of their verses are worth printing.

Smith.—Yet it is right that the young of this war should be printed. I should feel as little impulse to criticise them as I would to dissect the two or three weak notes, endlessly repeated, of a February bird. If I read them, shouldn't I feel the same momentary anguish, the same memories, so close, so lost, of childhood, the same despair at the thought of dying and losing all I saw, as moved the writers ? Emotions which have as little to do with the poem as with the bird's twittering — nothing, in fact, except the occasion. And if one of these young becomes all at once mature, a poet, it can only be because his death is taking the place in him of his ignorance, uncertainties, mistakes, his joys, the serious illness of his son, his conversion, voyages, arthritis, his old age. . . . All these voices I can hear entering and leaving your ears, they are the same voices of my friends ; the past is still breathing ; the same seeds fall into the same furrows. How well I understand the anxiety of you and your friends not to vanish without having been noticed. I, too, pushed my lips out to catch a drop of that immortality which tastes so differently from anything I expected.

Green.—It seems to me that what I taste is very faintly salt, as though the sea were not far off.

Smith.—Wait, wait. . . . Tell me whether you and your friends thought of us at all. What did you think ?

Green.—That we are not like you, that if we could talk to

you about war you would exasperate us and we you, that our lives, from our childhood, have been different, less simple, older than yours. I remember the lines written by one of us—

For us
No voice will speak in the white cemeteries
Of France. We are not of that careless kind
To whom life seemed to offer prize on prize,
Who, at the terminus, with laughing eyes
Saw only joy in battle. Blind, stark blind.

Not very good verses, but they rhyme a feeling most of us have.

Smith.—Who has been telling you lies about us ?

Green.—For you, the war was a crusade, it excited you ; and you had a faith, you believed you were saving something. To us from our childhood the thought of war was unspeakably boring, and often frightening. It made us angry and nervous. We have seen how little it can save. When it began we fought because we had to, because it seemed the thing to do. We were never eager to go.

Smith.—But who tells you that we were ? All my friends, all of them, and I too, went regretfully and at once, feeling we had to, that it was the thing to do. We may have been simpler than you, but we were not blind or careless. And how bored we were. My God, how bored. . . . There is a difference. We were less sorry for ourselves. . . . And another — you expected it. And if you thought of the future — I don't think we thought about it, we only longed for it, the present was so boring, such an excruciating waste of our time — I have no doubt you thought of it in a more explicit way. But your backward glance regrets all the things we regretted, your senses are identical with ours — and your memories. No, no, you have been deceiving yourselves, you are like us. And we, too, thought, but without pride, that we were a marked generation.

Green.—Tell me — did you, in a moment of danger or afterwards, feel sometimes an extreme pleasure only in living — so that the smell of bread or to taste it was positively exciting ?

Smith.—Yes.

Green.—I used to pray to keep it, if I survived.

Smith.—I did that, too. I know now that if I had lived,

life would have been more like *this* than like that. . . . War is more exacting than at the time it seems. . . .

At this moment, another young soldier appears in the doorway of the room, which opens on the yard. They see, from his uniform, that he is a Czech. Smith feels that something on which this stranger was relying for his life has given way, and he hurries to speak, though long since he has discovered the crudity, because of their obstinate logic, of words.

Smith.—Were you looking for us?

Czech.—No. I saw the house and it reminded me of one I know very well. Now that I look at it closely I see I was deceived by a doorway, and a tree near it. In fact I can scarcely see it. . . . I — it confuses me.

Smith.—Use my eyes. Here are two chairs, a window, a mirror, here is a sofa. Stay until you feel quiet.

Green.—Why are you here? Your country is not at war. You were well out of it.

Czech.—Is that what you others think? . . . Show me anything you like of the vileness of war, I will show you something far darker — a rational terrorism, cold, deliberate, wounding parents through the torture of their children, the dreadful mutilation of prisoners, the destruction of reason in the very minds of the ruled. You have never seen cruelty.

Green.—Not so close. Not clearly. There is a real difference between you and us. It came into the room with you, and I saw that I, and my friends, and this soldier of 1914, are all ignorant beside you. Your nerves themselves know more than ours — the human violin remembering what has been played on it.

Smith.—Here we shall soon be alike. At first, one is nothing but memory, time has no longer an existence except as memories, and all one's care is to keep them distinct and separate, not to fall headlong into the stream and lose consciousness with desire. It is not easy. From all sides, from every level of one's past life, from every flight of a desire once flown if only for a second, things call out demanding to be seen, listened to. . . . Because of the new war, and the deaths, this house called me again. . . . But already I begin to guess at something other than memory, or at another memory. It has happened to me to return to a French town I know well, Le Mans, and find myself looking at a house, small, poor, in flames, and at a woman dying beside her dead children, while soldiers speaking a language only vaguely familiar were burning and killing in other houses in the same street. Then I realised that I was seeing one of those incidents, of a siege followed by a massacre of all the inhabitants, described by Froissart as briefly as one of our communiqués describes the sinking of a ship or the wiping out of a battalion. The strange — or is it not so strange ? — thing is that so many of these memories which are peculiarly mine are of cruelty and violence — as though it were these, and not the simple joys or the complicated ecstasies, cling most strongly to our skeletons or to the earth.

Green.—I wish I understood cruelty.

Smith.—I begin to think it is one of the prime movers, a tool of evolution. Unconscious in animals, already half conscious in human beings, when it becomes fully conscious perhaps our horror will get the better of our attraction and we shall renounce it.

Czech.—My mind darkens when these things are spoken of. It has happened to me often in the last year, my nineteenth, to think of suicide, so great has been my horror in having anything in common, even a body, with men who could do what I have seen and heard of men doing in the concentration camps in my country.

Green.—I can't imagine wanting to kill myself. I regret, and bitterly, the separation from my body. It seems to me now that I made it myself, and with such care. I remember trivial things about it, not even pleasurable, how it stood in the broiling sun at a cross-roads, hot, dusty, sweating in its clumsy uniform, and how it talked to someone, and laughed. I almost feel grief. Who can be crying, so close to me, if it is not myself ?

Moving to the door, he stands looking out, and suddenly leaves them. With a smile, Smith turns to the young Czech.

Smith.—No doubt he's gone home. His friends, or a lover, have called him — or his mother's house. One or other of these always speaks first.

Czech.—Really ? I hope not. If I told you what had become

of my nearest friend and of my father and brother, you would beg them not to speak to me. I shall stay here, in this country which did not want me and has nothing to say to me. I don't care to remember the Vltava which was the first natural thing to teach me that light flows and turns on itself and plays like a river, nor the dark street in Prague which spoke to me of sunlight, nor the stones which are my heart beating——

Smith.—Take care ! You won't be able to save yourself from anything you risk thinking about. . . .

But the Czech has gone. Left alone, Smith touches the wall of the house gently, with a casual friendliness.

Smith.—Until next time you need me. . . . Was I, perhaps, born only to save a few very ordinary things from dying — this house ; the eggs, a dozen of them, I sat whisking in a kitchen bowl so that my mother could skim the froth into the birthday cake she was making ; the very old may-tree, as tall and thick as an oak, two grown together, under which we played — we called it The Tree ; the Grass of Parnassus in the red earth of the cliff, so strong, so delicate, its gleaming white veined with purple ; the cliff-top itself, rough fields not defaced, as now, by houses ; and the harbour — above all, the harbour, between its hills, its old roofs, its few ships, humble and useful. . . . Dear, how dear, deepest love of my body and mind. Yet help me to forget, to go farther, to go on.

*

Certains des " problèmes " qui nous agitent sont, non point certes insignifiants, mais parfaitement insolubles — et suspendre notre décision à leur solution est folie. Donc passons outre. — Les Nouvelles Nourritures.

*

1943

6 January. Harlech lies, clings, rather, between the sea and a country of severe beauty. The coast on which I was born is not unlike this. But there I was — I am — in everything. This country is as alien as Budapest — or so it feels to me. More alien, since there I was in Europe. Here, one is no longer in Europe, the hills, among the oldest anywhere, reject Europe, and in their soft voices the people speak a language which owes Europe nothing.

It rains a great deal here, but on the days when you can see the country it offers the stranger everything except its confidence, everything he sees. This country is a long afternoon when the sea, peacock-coloured, is parted by a cone formed of flakes of light, whirling and falling between the sky and the edge of the sand, where are long ribs of light ; the near flakes are larger than stars, shifting, going out, reappearing, soundless explosions of light in the sea itself ; where the point of the cone touches the horizon a pure light ; the sun moves, and the storm of light moving with it over the bay, clever as a flight of birds, is gone : it is the estuary, claimed by the wind-moulded and barren hills : it is the great line, colour of pollen, of evening, flowing round the horizon and below the hills planted at the other, the remote edge of the bay ; they are cut off by it from the sea, and they float, paler than a pale sky, between it and this lying impure light : it is the sun when it drops towards the sea, elongated and deformed, pulled out of shape by all that weight of barred and bronze water, and throws a strong doubt on the truth of violet sands and a sky as many-coloured as a circus : it is the rainbow spouting from the sea between two waves : above all, it is the hills, the small and great hills, abolished by the light.

Mine is a mind bound fast to the body, to what it sees. Like those who gave me life, I live in my eyes. It follows that no one is less awake to voices from the other, invisible, side of life. When rarely I hear such a voice it forces its way upwards through a weight of rock and earth, and is too strong for me. I am a savage whose god has spoken. Since I came here, every night when I lie down, the idea of death steps into my mind. It is an idea, a sensation, not an image. During the day it vanishes completely ; I forget it ; I work. As soon as I have turned the light out at night and lain down to sleep — I sleep well — before I have had time to expect it, it is there. Yes, it forces its way in. But then if it did not I should hear nothing.

I ignore it as much as possible. This moment is the first I have reasoned about it. Either it has stepped into the room

left when my fear of failure became indifference to failure : or
it is that old anger which seized me when, very young, I reflected that one day I should no longer be able to look at the
world.

But it is not anger ; and not a fear. It is as if sound were
coming from the mute notes of a piano. I hear an absence of
sound and translate it to mean death. Whose death, close to
me at this moment, is troubling me — such trouble as I allow
myself to overhear ? My own, surely ? — but why ? I am not
so ill.

I have a book to finish.

*

24 February. It is not true that, two weeks ago, an air-raid
killed my young sister ; it is not true that she alone, of the five
or six persons in the kitchen of the communal restaurant, was
killed when a bomb demolished the place. She was a volunteer
worker — a part of her war work — and when the bomb fell,
since there were no other sounds, no gun-fire, she must have
heard it come. It is not true that you don't hear the bomb
which is going to fall near you. One of those daylight raids of
single planes. Flying at a great height, they loose their bombs
on some small unguarded town and make off. What are they ?
Young men making a practice flight ?

It is not true that she is dead. The image of her, young
resigned mouth, lips parted, as if to drink at a stream, and her
poor face, a little disfigured, is not clearer than the others, smiling
and fresh. When old people die, surely with nothing left to
want, unless it were another sunny afternoon to slip in among
all those they have been gathering since childhood, one's anguish
is without disbelief — even without despair. But there was so
much she wanted. To see her children again ; to work, to use
her quick rather short fingers, young restless hands ; to make
plans. She planned as she moved, with the pure energy of
delight. From everything of hers we touched, afterwards, it
was the future sprang out. Even, expecting that in a long war
there would soon be no such frivolities, she had bought the
cards for three more birthdays — for a boy of seven, eight,
nine, and a girl five and six and seven. And there were all the

other things she had prepared for them, going with her little money into shops and spying out what might please them or they would be sure to need. The festival their return was to be . . . and her gaiety hoarded to be spent on them.

Why, God, take one so filled with the future? You could have taken me and that column of the past I am becoming. Why, why?

Is it possible she is not still learning and working somewhere, she who worked ceaselessly from the moment she drew herself out of her deep dreamless sleep in the morning until the night, when she went late to bed, leaving with regret some of her tasks unfinished? Is it possible?

*

I have to remind myself of what has happened. There is not a nerve in my body which consents to it. And now I know that what we say of the young dead, *They shall not grow old*, says only that the agony of their solitary going away remains, unchanged by time. The future does not spring from it, as it sprang from the laid table, and from the places where, under a handkerchief or among books, she had hidden it. Nothing wears it down. And think that so many young are being hurried out of life before they have grown used to it, and this pain, this glacier, is covering Europe with its cold — where we have to live.

*

She rejoiced in her tireless acts, and the young gestures of her body. And now all of her which was action lives in our minds, nowhere else. The other, the dream which slept in her, disinterested in all she was always doing, is where? What journey is it making, through what country it recognises and which knows it?

I dreamed of her. "Oh, my little love, your clothes, we have given away all your clothes."

"Not those I wear," she said, smiling.

*

Under the young sun, and for a few minutes, these hills put

off their terrestrial bodies and become spirits or forms, the colour of sleep. My young sister's death has destroyed in me the fear of dying, but left the fear, unappeased, of another's defeat. For this there is no cure, and one should not seek a cure. It could be found only by a refusal to live.

But this refusal. . . . I should not be making it — surely? — if I avoid the social and half-public life which is a torment to me. And increasingly so hard to carry off that I have sometimes wondered whether I am, as we say, *all there*. Am I?

There is always in the background this one occupied with *l'inanité de son famélique cauchemar*. I can hold my mind together, and turned to the light coming from outside, long enough to talk to one or a few friends or a few strangers (or non-friends, which is not the same), and make them believe I am sane and intelligent. But not more, or for very long.

Is it possible to accept cruelty and death, and remain curious about the world? For me, yes — I have a double dose of curiosity. The silence will hurry me off long before I have exhausted my pleasure simply in looking — which no self-discipline, improbable enough, could lessen to the benefit of this other pleasure in the prose, deliberately unmelodious, broken into discords, and expressive, of Mallarmé. My eyes, a little staring, have worn themselves on the world and its images, but the images which have clouded them came from the other half of life. To cure myself of a sense of absence, almost intolerable, I have tried to add myself to the world, and I have a handful of memories. But very small — you couldn't speak of it as a world. Not even when you have taken up into the account all those inner changes and constructions which — how much time I wasted — are almost nothing.

And the images of the world? — are they not safely among the inner creations? Of course. They are my happy life. I am ignorant about joy — since it belongs to the use of the senses and, led by hazard, I use only one of mine. But who supposes that a joyless life must be unhappy? Only those who do not know what words mean. I believe that I should be even happier if I chose to give up the life of action and seeing, and tried to complete a few of those invisible constructions which hold, or seem to, the meaning of change. It would be a refusal, another. The change is always from life to memory.

*

It is not surprising how often my memories have the form and colour of France : *cette terre lumineuse, discrète et subtile*, has already the quality of a living idea. The real France is too complex, perhaps too exacting, to be carried in the mind or to be loved. Directed by memory, I reach easily a France of warmth, perfume, light. *On n'arrive jamais à la mort sans dot* : when my dower is looked at by death's persevering solicitors they will find, among the rest, a July night with the word Mâcon, and the word *mânes*, written under it : for a time they will be able to make out the Saône, the colour of doubt, and the flat shuttered houses — you would say they are only appearances — on the other bank. Perhaps a taste lingers of the white strawberries, peaches, raspberries, small grapes, of the meal, or of a sauce which has barely thought of garlic. Then darkness, and the feeble light of the street-lamps along the quay becomes the life-blood of millions of spectral moths, their bodies, a long fibre dividing transparent wings, invisible except for the veins : they fall together under the lighted window in cloudy heaps, moved by a creaking breath when the night air from the Saône touches their dryness.

There were so many that they infested the night ; in the morning, except for those caught in the ironwork of balconies and a handful of dust, they were gone. I asked the porter of the hotel whether they had a name. " Of course," he said curtly, " we call them *mânes*." I did not know what he meant until I remembered,

> *Je vois, je vois flotter, fuyant l'honneur des chairs*
> *Des mânes impuissants les millions amers. . . .*

Mâcon has a sinister history of violence and sieges, beginning in barbarian times and lasting until the end of the sixteenth century.

Seldom, before the cold of these years, have I felt the strength of my longing for the heat of France, that stillness of the heat which reaches from the dry ground to the sky, isolating, from the useless movement of time, it may be a vast shabby square like the Place d'Armes in La Rochelle, or the whole of some obscure small town, or a road in the Landes. The heat holds everything within it immobile, porous to the silence. The images bring with them . . . and split open like husks to show their seeds . . . their own reflections of colour and the power of the sun over France. They are often the images not of a familiar place, but of shabbily cream-washed walls, as in the Grande Place — how small, with its arcades, how quiet, with its fringe of hills (and in the mountain villages higher up the roofs are weighted by stones) — of Thônes. There is an amazing dignity in many of these small towns, with the sense of a composed unified life, not dependent on some city or arterial road. The road to Thônes from the valley and the lac d'Annecy lies between meadows and trees, so many trees.

And not only the warmth of France, but the perfume of France, and the light, the pure pollen of the light, helping at the birth of vines and ideas. It so happens that both images are reflected for me from a river. From three rivers, Loire, Gironde, Dordogne. What, when I have named them, comes towards me and asks, smiling, to be caressed and given life ? At Bourg-sur-Gironde, in the worn square with the church, the steps leading far down and steeply to the river, the fig-tree below the lip of the wall, the lime-trees of the square — it is the last week of June — release the first hesitant notes of a phrase which will be taken up again by the Dordogne at Libourne, and between Libourne and St. Pey d'Armens render, in the massive light, the double reverberation of perfume and bees. What honey in a phrase ! And at Saumur — again June — the Loire has had the idea of coming without sun, freed from the interference of the sun passing between the sky and the surface of the water, the pure reflection of light, flowing through its own images of stone embankment and modest houses : serpents of light move along it and plunge for ever ; the one following is not the same. Always new beginning and no end. The illusion, life ceaselessly casting its bright skin, is complete. . . .

O Loire, O Dordogne, O Gironde, I need only touch you with my fingers for my thirst to be stilled.

*

Sleep, sleep ; the temples lie beneath the hands
On the warm earth and where the towers sprang
The roots turn and twist, and the voices sang
Where silence rises, falls, rises, the sands
Are not so cold if deep, deep, in the land's
Throat a source softly denies the pang
Of earth on the eyes . . . and the viper's fang
Bites harmlessly where only a leaf stands.
Who lives ? The one stooping to the spring
Now, or the others, suppliant, who cling
To the roots and speak close to me ? . . . the voice
Climbs in me an obscure path to rejoice
In the young light ripening the seeds of sight. . . .
Under the closed lids the night is not night.

*

I have learned that honours — *au pluriel, au pluriel*, Péguy mocks — give no pleasure unless they can be taken home to a family. In this, the approbation of strangers is not worth very much. Even Péguy — do not doubt it — would have been pleased with one or two quite small honours he could have taken home to the house in Orléans. A deep instinct, unless we have been spoiled, makes us wish to please, with these bright useless things, the eyes which are like but not ours . . . since they are worth nothing in themselves . . . and, without a family, we have nowhere to put them.

*

Let us suppose that the first effort one makes in life — later on, when the impatient and half-blind will comes in to help, nothing will be as thoroughly and well done — is to learn a few or one or two things by heart. Love at first sight or hearing or touch. In me, always deaf (under my acute hearing) and awkward, sight. Thus they are never lost ; possibly they are all we came to look for and take away. Although now I cannot look at them with eyes which reflect them directly, not distorted by greed or the fear of loss, on to my young spirit (not even then clear), I know that with the help of my body — was it indispensable ? — I have given them a second chance of life. And how much gentleness and strength even a child has at its disposal. Nothing can rob me of these things : the lighted windows, few and modest, a handful fallen together in the softly immense darkness, of my town ; the shadowy arm of the coast at night, consoling ; the moor road, imagined between scarcely seen lights of two farms, the last on those bare hills ; the rays of the sun embracing, when it has fallen to exactly their level in the opposite quarter of the sky, the Parish Church and, round it, leaning over, bleached by the sea wind, all those dumb stones ; the blazing whiteness of marguerites entering the eyes at their height of the child buried in the long grass. Night, evening, noonday. In what order will they leave me, last of all carefully-formed realities, last of all images — and my body the link between them ? . . .

I have been living alone in a village farther up the estuary, at the foot of the hills. After a day of trying, with great effort, to write, I went out to walk in the dusk, which here in August lasts so long and changes so slowly into night that at no moment can you feel it is the end of the day. The sky was still blue, with white vaporous clouds, yet there were stars. The light not clear — and by that all the more noticeable. Where it clung to things it could be seen.

I walked at the side of the estuary. Slowly, that resistance I put up, always, all my life, and without, perhaps, willing it, against being taken possession of was gone, and all I could see entered into me : the trees took strange shapes and entered in, and the mountains on either side, the river, the ambiguous light it reflected and gave back changed, the remote clouds, the wind stroking my face — all these blew into me and through me. And if these, I thought, can, why not the dead ? Why cannot I see walking with me that young woman, in her haste leaning a little forward, as I do, and the young airman, still a boy, with the blue clouded eyes, and that old captain, shabby, awkward, he whose voyages have eaten into him with the strictness of salt, and that woman, with her remote gaze, who reappears in me

again and again, to tell me — and at times I have the strength to
disobey her — what to feel and how I must act ? Why don't
they come ? What must I do to be more defenceless, to be
less, than I was in these moments ?

As I walked I said : Look, I give myself to you.

But what good is that when at once I take myself back again ?
When, in me, someone, a child, always begins again.

THE END

Printed in Great Britain by R. & R. CLARK, LIMITED, *Edinburgh*